ALEXANDER McKEE is twenty books on aspects of military, naval and aeronautical history, and on the search for buried wrecks. He flew his first aeroplane while still in his 'teens, and it was only inadequate vision that kept him out of the RAF. The son of a surgeon commander in the Royal Navy, he has spent most of his life on or under the sea, and still lives near Portsmouth, where he is an Honorary Life Member of the Southsea Branch of the British Sub-Aqua Club. His work on locating and excavating the Tudor warship *Mary Rose* brought him an OBE and international fame. His most recent books include *Dresden 1945: The Devil's Tinderbox*, *How We Found the Mary Rose*, *The Golden Wreck: The Tragedy of the 'Royal Charter'*, and revised editions of *Caen: Anvil of Victory* and *From Merciless Invaders: The Defeat of the Spanish Armada*.

WITHDRAWN

THE MOSQUITO LOG

Alexander McKee

MORAY
DISTRICT
LIBRARY

47192

Futura

17792

MORAY
DISTRICT
LIBRARY
SERVICE

623.7464

A Futura Book

Copyright © 1988 by Alexander McKee
First published in Great Britain in 1988 by
Souvenir Press Ltd,
43 Great Russell Street,
London WC1

This Futura edition published 1989

All Rights Reserved. No part of this publication
may be reproduced, stored in a retrieval system,
or transmitted, in any form or by any means, electronic,
mechanical, photocopying, recording or otherwise without
the prior permission of the Copyright owner

ISBN 0 7088 4260 7

Printed and bound in Great Britain by
Hazell, Watson & Viney Ltd
Aylesbury, Bucks

Futura Publications
A Division of
Macdonald & Co (Publishers) Ltd
Greater London House
Hampstead Road
London NW1 7QX

A member of Maxwell Pergamon Publishing Corporation plc

*RAF Badge on Title Page Crown Copyright. Reproduced by
permission of the Controller, Her Majesty's Stationery Office*

Contents

Preface

I am really glad that somebody is at last tackling the story of the Mosquito from the human side, not just a collation of Mark numbers, technical data, production figures and lists of operational units. It is the men who flew them, serviced them–and were 'on the receiving end' that really matter in history!

Letter by Alex Vanags-Baginskis to the author, 1987

Alex's letter, quoted above, sums up exactly my intentions in writing this book, with the proviso that in my appeals for assistance I asked also for testimony from the men and women who designed and made the Mosquito.

The response was tremendous and I am deeply grateful to all who helped. It seemed that the time was right to preserve and pass on their memories. The result was that I could confidently plan a book which consisted 98 per cent of fresh material, and of the most varied nature, because what was originally designed as an unarmed evader bomber became one of the most versatile aircraft in history. From its inception in 1938 at Hatfield to its last operational flights in 1958, over the Sinai desert, the story of the Mosquito, as told mostly in the words of participants, is one of the most remarkable in aviation, and I am infinitely grateful to them all for their help.

Alexander McKee
Hayling Island, Hampshire,
August, 1987.

CHAPTER ONE

Born Among the Bombs

You must bear in mind that anyone like myself is taxing the memory of 47 years and could be suspect in minute details, but when you gather a number of reports together you should be able to complete a very accurate account.

Letter by L. F. Waller to author, 1987

More than twenty witnesses of the bombing of the De Havilland aircraft factory at Hatfield, north of London, contacted me. All but one told basically the same story, with variations according to where they were and what they were doing on the morning of 3 October, 1940. The sole exception, Kenneth Jarvis, did not claim to be a witness but had seen what he thought was the return of the raiders:

I was in a small workshop in Finchley, North London, some 12 miles due south of Hatfield, and had become used to the sound of gunfire and aircraft. I cannot remember the date, but it was a beautiful summerlike day when we heard, what was not usual: the sound of what appeared to be a continuous roll of thunder lasting about a minute. The continuous roar of explosions was clearly not from just one plane and was heard inside our workshop. Some ten minutes later we heard the roar of a large number of aircraft flying together and the sound of diving aircraft and machine-gun fire, and we went into the street to watch. We could see above us some twelve German aircraft, being attacked by two Spitfires. The formation, which I thought to be of Heinkel 111s, was travelling due east towards Edmonton, Walthamstow and East London. I can only guess at the height as being about 8 to 10,000 feet; the aircraft, although small, were clearly visible. Although one German aircraft was smoking I saw no aircraft actually shot down. There was great excitement in what was in wartime a quiet suburban street. A group of dustmen were emptying bins opposite; their cheers and shouts of encouragement to the Spitfire pilots was good to hear. The battle drifted towards the east–just another event of our wartime days. But you can be sure that the formation I saw attacked Hatfield.

This is such a good description of a typical day in London during September 1940, that I include it; but although the German formation must have attacked a target near Hatfield, this was clearly quite a different raid and quite a different day. Everyone else described a single raider–a Junkers Ju 88–popping out of low cloud on a day when even the birds were walking.

Mary Anderson was a student at Oaklands Institute of Agriculture, a mile or two from the De Havilland factory:

The plane came towards the aerodrome from an easterly direction at tree-top height. I assumed it was a British bomber until the German markings were clear. I always understood the observers on the roof were late giving the warning because, like myself, they thought it was a British plane.

Mr L. F. Waller was then a 26 year-old aircraft inspector working for De Havilland at shop-floor level, checking acceptability of manufactured parts:

On that particular morning the weather was atrocious,

8

low damp fog everywhere, so that there was no flying of any description from the aerodrome. I was in the Wood Mill at the time, which was so noisy from the machines that no one had any idea of what was going on outside. The foreman, Mr George Stredwick, had been outside giving instructions to his charge-hand in the Wood Sheds about 50 yards away. I was by the door of the Mill when he returned, and heard him ask our senior inspector, Mr Tom Clark, if there was any test flying that day, as he was sure that he had seen an aircraft fly very low over the factory, and was also positive it had German markings on it. A man was immediately sent down to the Erecting Shop, a walk inside the factory, to establish if there was any flying that day.

The general air raid warning by siren was not sounded anywhere near the aerodrome, but factories often had their own local warning and lookout systems, for very often, when the sirens did sound, nothing happened–the raiders passed over or passed by or turned back. The newly recruited 'Roof Spotters' were responsible for giving warning to staff only in the event of actual, identified danger.

We had a lookout post on top of the factory, which was manned all the time, but in that weather, although they would hear an aircraft, it would be difficult to see unless it was very close. We had no knowledge of an attack until the factory klaxon was sounded for immediate 'take cover'–three to four minutes after the sighting by our foreman, Mr Stredwick. We had air raid shelters built inside the factory to give some form of immediate cover, and dugouts below ground outside the factory. I elected to use a dugout outside and had just reached it when the bombs dropped.

9

Before the war we used to admit foreign students into our Technical School, and it seemed common knowledge that the plane's pilot was an ex-student who knew the area well. It appeared that when he crossed the coast he must have flown very low all the way until he found the Great North Road which, if followed, would lead him to Hatfield and the factory. When first seen he must have been confirming his position; he then skirted the aerodrome round to the Aero Engine Factory from the St Albans side. Whether by design or mistake, you could see afterwards that when the bombs were released they dropped first on the edge of the soft grass aerodrome and bounced on their sides before hitting the 94 Shop and exploding at floor level, causing maximum blast damage. That part of the factory was isolated from the rest and completely flattened. In spite of the bad shake-up, everyone, no matter who they were, volunteered to do any job that needed doing, and in no time at all large sections of the factory were back in production once again.

Security, on the 'need to know' principle, was so good that to this day most of the people who saw the bombing have no idea exactly how serious the damage was. Denis Austen was at Hatfield doing his elementary flying training course on Tiger Moths (which were also being built at the factory there, plus the engines for them):

We could not understand why security was so intense, including one hangar which was locked and under 24-hour full guard. However, on that particular morning the weather was so bad that our Tiger Moths were grounded–even the pigeons were on morning parade. If my memory serves me–it's 47 years ago–between 11 a.m. and 12 noon my RAF

10

course were going from one lecture room to another, with cloud base at about 200 feet, and were all on the tarmac when out of the clouds came a Ju 88, all guns blazing. The man next to me–name of Bloxam–was hit in the hand. We all dived into the slit trench shelters and heard bombs exploding and then the sound of an aircraft crashing–it was all over in a few seconds. As far as I know the Ju 88 was shot down by light flak and not Home Guard rifle fire. I must say it was a remarkable piece of flying and navigation by the German crew who obviously knew what they were after. However, they missed that guarded hangar and dropped their bombs about one mile away. I think that all of us respected the navigation and guts of the crew in appalling weather.

Austen had remembered the time correctly: it was indeed about 11.30 a.m. Denis MacManus, now aged 77, who was in charge of the engine and propellor development test beds on the far north-western side of the aerodrome, also recalled the bad flying conditions:

The day was misty with poor visibility and all aircraft, test pilots, RAF Tiger Moth trainers and Air Transport Auxiliary, were grounded; all our aircraft were inside with hangar doors closed. Therefore it seemed surprising to see an aeroplane coming in low as if to land. Ten minutes earlier I had spoken on the phone to the foreman of the coppersmiths about some work to be done in my test beds, after which I drove over to the factory with a technical assistant, Bill Mason, in my car. As I approached the tarmac I saw a frontal angle of the twin-engined aircraft coming in low over the far hangars from the south-east, and said to my colleague: 'It looks as though he is going to land with his wheels up.' Then the aircraft veered off

11

north-east and at about 100 feet it was obviously a Ju 88 displaying a 'dirty great swastika' on its tailfin. I immediately did a U-turn, shouted to the nearby RAF anti-aircraft gun crew and, two minutes later, back at my office, phoned the security officer. For reasons not known to me the factory warning system was not operated until the Ju 88 was back over the airfield five to ten minutes later.

The German pilot was, I thought, extremely courageous and highly skilled in flying the aeroplane at very low altitude. On a right-hand circuit he reappeared again from the south-east, this time with bomb doors open. At a height of about 100 feet and flying close to stalling speed, he aligned his aircraft with the power house chimney, by which time several machine-guns were blazing away from our RAF ground crews and, probably, the German air gunners as well.

The stick of four bombs dropped flat onto the grass airfield, bouncing into the factory workshop which exploded in fragments to a height of about 300 feet and then subsided–all seemingly in slow motion. The Ju 88 veered off in a northerly direction and was brought down in a field a few miles away. A large number of factory employees were killed, including the foreman who I was on my way to visit.

Mr L. F. Waller, the aircraft inspector, recalled that:

The building known as the 94 Shop, which received direct hits, was completely flattened and burnt out. The small building adjacent, known as the Technical School for students, was put completely out of action. The rest of the factory nearest to the hits received blast damage, as a large area had corrugated iron roofing and sliding doors to the airfield,

12

but I cannot recall any fires in this area.

The 94 Shop was so called because up to the war it had been used for production of the DH 94, known as the Moth Minor, which was a light civil monoplane designed for the business man and selling at £575. The first Moth, the DH 60, of 1925, was generally called the Cirrus Moth, while the much better known Tiger Moth, the DH 82, dated from 1931. Most of the Moth series were of wooden construction, at which De Havilland's were expert. But the 94 Shop was no longer producing 94s: it was instead being switched to the DH 98, the very latest in the long line of De Havilland aircraft and, for once, a warplane.

Leslie Frost, now 73, worked then in the Toolroom and was the leader of a four-strong First Aid Party:

The klaxon went, and I grabbed my tin hat and first aid kit, shot through the hole in the steel fence round the Toolroom, and was outside the building almost on my own. I glanced over my shoulder, and coming in fast was a huge black plane with two propellors and machine-guns firing. I didn't wait. My own trench (a huge, galvanised iron semi-circular shelter covered with earth and grass, holding 50 people) was right across the 'drome, too far to run, so I ran to the nearest, Trench 8. Four of us arrived at the steps together, and together we jumped into the trench, landing in a heap on the floor. While we lay there we could hear the machine-gun bullet spatting on the iron of the trench roof through the earth. After about 20 minutes a motor cycle despatch rider called down to us:'Any first aiders, come with me', and we were taken to the 94 Shop.

I cannot describe the scene. Large fires, smoke, debris, lumps of concrete everywhere, and we with our little fireman's axes chopping away. I understand

13

50 people were killed and 100 injured, although some of the injuries were minor, such as my own–I ran a nail into my foot. A shelter inside the building, comprising single brick walls supporting a heavy concrete roof, collapsed onto some people, crushing them to death. I saw benches, similar to ours in the Toolroom. Men had sheltered under them and presumably their muscles had contracted as there were multiple compound fractures everywhere and many, many bones sticking out, up to four inches. There was no blood. Quite the reverse, they looked ash-grey, dry, dusty and unreal.

One of the first surprises of the 'Blitz' was the discovery of blast effect, so peculiar that much ordinary first aid was pointless. The jagged streams of high-pressure air bursting out from the explosion like the unpredictable spurts of water from a tap when a finger is held over it, had the force of a motor car moving at speed; the effect was most noticeable inside buildings which had been directly hit, trapping for a moment the compressed air. Internal organs, such as lungs, liver and spleen, could be ruptured, so that no external bleeding was apparent and the victim died often with no apparent wound. The massive artillery bombardments of the First World War had not convincingly revealed the effect, partly because soldiers usually wore a lot of equipment on their bodies, and partly because a shell consists of a thick steel casing containing not very much explosive, whereas most bombs had thin casings surrounding a great deal of explosive. (The earliest discussions of this subject that I know of are in the *British Medical Journal* for 5 April, 1941: pp 506-510, 'Pulmonary Concussion ("Blast")', and pp 523-525, 'London Under Air Bombardment: Some Medical Aspects'.)

Harold N. Altman was stationed on Hatfield aerodrome with 145 Battery of 42 Light Anti-Aircraft Regiment, whose commanding officer was Colonel (later Sir) Mortimer Wheeler, the famously flamboyant archaeologist. One did not question his re-creation of, for instance, the scenes following the storming of Maiden Castle by the Romans in about AD 44, because he had seen a good deal of the real thing in AD 1940-45. Despite rival claims, it was probably his guns that got the Ju 88.

We could hear the sound of a plane over the aerodrome and our Bofors guns were alerted. It was a day of very low cloud and we were not able to get our sights on it. Quite suddenly, we saw the nose of a Ju 88 coming out of the clouds, we fired and it was brought down near St Albans. The pilot said that he knew exactly where he should bomb, as he had been employed in the Works Department of De Havilland's before the war. I noted this event in my diary, which unfortunately was lost in the Western Desert. There was some dispute at the time as to whether the plane was shot down by Bofors or by small arms fire from the De Havilland Home Guard, but Denis White, who was with me at Hatfield at the time, and I are convinced that it was the Bofors.

Don Harrison, who had been with the impromptu rescue teams, was told, like many others, to go home as there were now too many helpers. Having been bombed out from their home in South London in September, he and his wife had found billets by the aerodrome and, to make it worse, his wife was expecting their first child in November. So, to calm her, he suggested they go into St Albans for a meal and a walk round the shops. The bus conductress told them that she had just dropped at the railway station an Ack-Ack gunner who had been given seven days leave for shooting down the Ju 88. Next day, Don heard Monty Barnes, the chief shop steward, call for an enquiry to find out how the lone aircraft had got

15

through without proper warning being given. Not long after, Don was working on a new aircraft–the DH 98.

Jack Arliss was a police officer at the Hatfield station, his job being to drive the Chief Constable's car. On this particular morning, however, his chief was engaged with an important visitor, the Inspector of Constabulary, so Jack was sent with another policeman to the corporation depot to load corrugated-iron sheeting (for the construction of air raid shelters) into a police van. The depot was alongside the railway line, which gave him an excellent view of almost everything that happened, because the German pilot, like most airmen at that time operating under low cloud, was following the railway tracks. He was about 40-50 feet up and only a few yards away. Jack could clearly see the swastika painted on the tail, but thought that perhaps it was a captured machine (knowing that De Havilland's repaired such aircraft). Then the rear-gunner fired a burst of about eight shots, which went into the corporation shed. Jack vividly recalled how a horse reared up in fear at the sound.

The JU 88 went on down the line towards Hatfield Station, flew past it and disappeared out of our sight. It was three-quarters of a mile from there to De Havilland's. There were Tiger Moths dotted around, and I suppose the German pilot saw them, and so turned and came back. We saw him rise up over the factory; and we saw the tin roof of the factory fly up higher than the plane. The Ju 88 came back towards us, with the starboard engine trailing a three-to-five yards long flame. It disappeared toward Hertford, gradually losing height. I jumped into the van with a War Reserve constable and drove back to HQ. There was a cloud of black smoke over the De Havilland factory.

Eventually, I picked up about four men with rifles and we went towards Hertford. The Ju 88 had made

16

a good landing in a field on high ground, which had woods on either side. It had skidded to the left and was still burning. The four men with rifles got out of the van and went into one of the woods, while I drove slowly down a track at the far side of that wood. At the end of the wood I saw a constable armed with a stick coming from the hill–funnily enough, his name was Wood–and he was pointing with his stick at the hedge which separated me from the field. So I got out of the van, crossed the grass verge and went through a gap in the hedge.

A few feet away were four Germans, sitting there quietly on the bank of a ditch. When they saw me, they stood up. The nearest man turned out to be the rear-gunner, and next to him the pilot–blond, big (about 6 ft 4 ins), and very well built. The other two were about 5 feet 7 or 8 ins. They looked white and distressed. Been told they'd be shot. They weren't armed, but were in uniform. All of them had some items of RAF clothing–boots, trousers–apparently issued to them out of stores left behind by the British at St Malo aerodrome.

A British Army vehicle had turned up, containing an officer and a driver, so we divided the Germans into two pairs. The two non-descripts were taken by the Army to Hertford Police Station, but the pilot and the gunner were mine. The gunner was cheeky, took off his cap and gave it to me, saying, 'Souvenir!' I told him to put it back on again. The pilot was more gentlemanly.

Jack Arliss took them both to Hatfield Police Station, where they were put in separate cells, with the doors open, so that Jack, out in the corridor, could keep an eye on both. They refused food and drink (apparently believing it might be poisoned), and were eventually fetched away, to Jack's recollection, by two elderly gentlemen from an intelligence unit at Cambridge.

P. S. Thompson, a young police constable, later to join the RAF, was on duty that evening at Hatfield, which was also the HQ of the Hertfordshire Constabulary. He remembers the interrogators as being a Flight Lieutenant and a Sergeant from an RAF intelligence unit. Possibly there were two interrogation teams, the second arriving much later in the day, after dark.

The Flight Lieutenant asked first to see the pilot, so I accompanied the RAF Sergeant to the cells.

The German pilot, a strapping fellow of well over six feet, was lying on the cell bed and had taken off his flying boots which he had placed on the floor by the side of the bed. As we entered the cell he sat up and commenced to put his boots on, but at this point the RAF Sergeant grabbed the boots and told him to walk in his stockinged feet. The Sergeant was a very small man, I would imagine he barely made 5 feet, but he pushed and literally dragged the burly German from the cell and down the corridor, periodically planting his RAF boot in the nether regions of the German pilot. It was rather a comical sight and the Sergeant obviously made no bones about his treatment of German aircrew. This was not his first encounter but in the light of the fact they had just killed 25 or so British civilians it was perhaps understandable.

I stayed in the room whilst the interrogation was in progress but as this took place in fluent German, I did not understand any of it. However, the F/Lt. filled me in with the story later. It appeared that the Junkers 88's target was in the vicinity of Reading but owing to the bad weather, the pilot got lost and was eventually hit by the Ack-Ack battery which was stationed at Roe Green on the outskirts of Hatfield.

Not wishing to crash land with his bombs on board, he jettisoned them, unfortunately over the De Havilland airfield.

Subsequently the casualties from De Havilland's were brought in by ARP ambulance to Hatfield Police Station, which could not take anywhere near all the bodies, and we had to use other accommodation in the Station. There were about 20 bodies and a basket full of little bits collected.

Mrs Violet Collom was a young wife of 24 with two children whose husband Richard, after ten years in the RAF, was now working at De Havilland's. Although on the Reserve, he had not been called back into the Service because he was on war work, repairing damaged RAF fighters. Violet lived at Welwyn Garden City, just north of Hatfield. She saw the German aircraft circle round but did not know until the middle of the afternoon that the factory had been bombed, when she was told by a neighbour.

My husband didn't come home and there was no message. About 7 p. m. a Police Inspector took me to the factory, where they were making lists, of those killed, and of those sent to the hospital. My husband's name was not on any list.

The Police Inspector said the airman was trained to fly at Hatfield Flying School. He cried, because he did not know what he had hit. He had been looking for a viaduct, but was himself hit by AA and so he pressed the button.

A bomb fell right in the middle of five men, who were in a discussion; they were blown to pieces and buried together in Hatfield cemetery with a commemorative stone. My husband was found with 19 other men on the floor of a canteen, clothed and with no outward wound. So I have been a widow

19

since the age of 24. I was given back my husband's clothes, jewellery and papers, plus six weeks' wages, and was awarded a war widow's pension: 39 shillings and threepence a week. Later, I worked part-time on making wings for Mosquitos.

Violet Collom's recollection of what the Police Inspector said to her about the German pilot's story matches closely what Mr G. R. Jones was told about it:

I remembered the reported quote from the pilot, something like, 'I tried to warn the works with machine-gun fire, and am sorry for the number killed and injured.'

It may be so, particularly if he had really worked at Hatfield before the war; but there is of course an alternative explanation: that he was not telling his interrogators the truth. Why should he? Indeed, one is warned to give only name, rank and number; but there must be a temptation to mislead (particularly with interrogators like that RAF Sergeant). The machine-gunning is routine protection for any dive-bomber or low-flying aircraft, a tactic to suppress ground fire.

Although the belief that the German pilot had been employed by De Havilland's before the war is persistent, it seems to have no basis. John Cunningham, who was to become one of the most brilliant of the night-fighter pilots, had also been a student at Hatfield at the relevant time, and he replied to a query by the present author:

I joined the De Havilland Technical School in 1935 and the only German who was a fellow student with me worked at Junkers throughout the war, finishing up as a POW with the Americans. I am unaware of any other German student and think it highly unlikely that the pilot of the Ju 88 had any connection with De Havilland's.

How this story originated is unknown; although logical, it must appear unlikely to anyone who knows how any armed force actually works, the square pegs almost invariably being directed to the round holes.

An equally abiding mystery is the tale told by Wing Commander Ira Jones, a pugnaciously patriotic little Welsh airfighter who claimed 40 victories over the Western Front in the Great War of 1914-1918, and always maintained (not too convincingly, I thought) that the Irishman Mannock was better than Richthofen, the Red Baron. In his book *Tiger Squadron* he describes flying from Andover to Hatfield in bad weather and poor visibility and, half an hour after landing, hearing Bofors guns in action and seeing a Ju 88 actually releasing its bombs, which were bouncing over the aerodrome. That was the morning of 3 October all right, so perhaps he crept in to the aerodrome unnoticed (or his memory played a trick and this was one inspection he made by car).

His arrival was a direct consequence of the Luftwaffe onslaught on the aircraft factories which had begun on 4 September. Wing Commander Jones had been summoned to the Ministry of Aircraft Production's new headquarters at Millbank, overlooking the Thames, shown a map pin-pointing all the factories which had been attacked and told: 'Lord Beaverbrook has decided that in future all airframes are to be taken away from the works as soon as they are completed and stored in dispersal.'

These raids had been most effective and occasionally humiliating. For instance, Lord Beaverbrook himself had been due to open the brand new factory of Cunliffe Owen at Eastleigh, near Southampton, when on 11 September the Messerschmitt 110s of Eprobrungsgruppe 210 had laid three out of the four sheds flat on the grass, killing

70 of the workers; thus rendering the Beaver's journey strictly unnecessary. As at Hatfield, there had been no warning–but with much less excuse–and there was savage rage among the relatives directed, not at the Germans, but at the government.

Now it had happened to Taffy Jones. Half an hour after his arrival in order to sort things out at De Havilland's, the Luftwaffe, with a single aircraft, had clean bowled him!

The strange thing is, that in his book he was too patriotic to mention it, or perhaps he did not even know. He admits that many people were killed, but omits all reference to the critical effect on production of the new, secret 'super bomber', then being prepared at Hatfield against the wishes both of the Air Ministry and of Bomber Command. The result of four 250 kg bombs from the Ju 88 was the destruction of 80 per cent of the materials already assembled for the production, if successful, of the new DH 98 unarmed wooden bomber. Lord Beaverbrook was to prove one of its few friends at first. But on 3 October, the prototype had not yet even flown.

Denis Austen, who had witnessed the raid while at Hatfield learning to fly Tiger Moths, and had now done his first solo, also saw the unveiling of the secret inside that hangar which was under 24-hour security guard. He did not recollect the date, but in fact it must have been 26 November, 1940:

I remember that on a beautiful day all our flying was cancelled after lunch and we had no lecture. Rumour abounded and we were all out on the tarmac when the hangar doors opened at about 2.30–3 p.m. and a strange-looking aircraft was wheeled out–our first glimpse of the Mosquito. Geoffrey de Havilland climbed in, started the engines and taxied to the far side of the aerodrome.

He opened up and started belting across the grass (no runway), then slapped the throttles back and came to a stop near where we were watching. The mechanics played around for about 20 minutes, then he taxied back to the far side, turned into wind, and then, after a few seconds, opened up all he had got and came belting back again, lifting the 'Mossie' off with about 100 yards of 'drome left. He disappeared into the distant sky and we all waited–but not for long. Suddenly he appeared at about 100 feet–flat out across the 'drome–went away into the distance, then came back and landed. If my memory serves me right–it's nearly 47 years ago–when the engines were stopped there was silence among us all. I think that somehow we all knew we had been privileged to see the first flight of a wonderful aeroplane.

CHAPTER TWO
Unarmed Bomber

On the way from Hatfield to Boscombe Down, doing 260 m.p.h., a USAAF P-38 Lightning fighter pulled alongside us 50 feet away. The pilot made a rude gesture. Duffil, who was piloting me, opened the throttles and just steamed away from him. I could see his surprise, even under goggles.

David King in conversation with author, 1987

When the Second World War broke out in September, 1939, the aeroplane was less than 40 years old. To be precise, the first flight in a heavier-than-air machine was made by Orville Wright in December, 1903. What was then called the 'Great War' began some ten years later, in 1914.

Geoffrey de Havilland, whose hobby was designing motor car and motor cycle engines, turned to aero engines in 1907 and made his first flight in an aeroplane of his own design in 1909. Like the Wright brothers in America, his first flight lasted only a few seconds but, unlike theirs, it terminated in a crash. Ah, well–back to the drawing board.

There were two basic drawbacks to all early experiments in powered flight. The engines of those days were weak and very heavy proportionate to the tiny power outputs they produced; and the test pilots (who were also the designers, manufacturers and sometimes engine-makers as well), had never been taught to fly on any sort of powered aircraft, let alone an experimental, untested machine. But Geoffrey de Havilland persevered and a year later, in 1910, successfully flew his new design. It rose 'several inches off the ground for about twenty yards', according to a witness.

So began the career of a master designer who was to produce the Mosquito–for two-and-a-half years the fastest aircraft of World War II–and the first British jet airliner, the Comet. From stick-and-string to the sound barrier in one lifetime.

The origins of the De Havilland aircraft company can be traced back to May 1914, when Geoffrey de Havilland was taken on as designer and test pilot by George Holt Thomas, a newspaper owner who had become interested in aviation and was building under licence the successful French Farman machines. Geoffrey had suggested that it would be cheaper to employ him to build original machines of his own design rather than pay the French for the right to build their 'box kites'. So he joined Holt Thomas's company, Airco, and somehow the first aircraft he worked on became known as the DH 1 (rather than the DHT 1). This was a pusher, with the engine behind to give a clear field of fire to a machine-gun in front. The DH 2 quickly followed, a very successful little single-seat pusher fighter, with which Major Hawker gained many victories until he was shot down by Manfred von Richthofen in a faster Albatros with a machine-gun firing through the arc of the airscrew.

When this little problem (of not shooting off your own propellor) was solved on the Allied side, Geoffrey de Havilland designed the DH 4 light bomber, a two-seater biplane, with one machine-gun firing forward and one or two Lewis guns on a flexible mounting in the back seat. This bomber was extremely fast, could outstrip any other bomber and give even single-seat fighters a run for their money. It was as a pilot of these in daylight raids into Germany that W. E. Johns got the air fighting experience which was to result in the creation of his famous character, 'Biggles'.

In 1933, aged 15, I had started learning to fly at

25

Portsmouth Aero Club, which was equipped with variants of the Moth–a most successful sports aircraft which was the foundation of the De Havilland company's fortunes in the difficult inter-war years. It was a very simple two-seater biplane with folding wings, just about small enough to squeeze into an ample garage. There were metal versions, but the ones we flew had a simple, box-structure fuselage made of plywood, the wings being of wooden framing covered by canvas. The distinctive smell of the dope used to tighten up the canvas, mingled with the scent of mown grass and engine oil, belong to that time in aviation.

The DH 60, as it was numbered, was a 1925 design powered by a 60 hp Cirrus I engine. I flew the later versions powered by the Cirrus II, the Gipsy I and Gipsy II, and finally the Moth Major, powered by a 130 hp Gipsy Major engine, this being my favourite. The Gipsy engines were also made by De Havilland. Just before the war, I got a chance to fly the DH 82 Tiger Moth (which, with a hood over the cockpit, we used for blind flying instruction) and also the rainproof DH 87 Hornet Moth–a side-by-side cabin two-seater. When World War Two began, these aircraft (but principally the Tiger Moth), plus the Oxford bomber trainers designed by Nevil Shute Norway and his team at the Airspeed factory at Portsmouth Airport, represented most of the output of the De Havilland factory at Hatfield. They had not designed an acceptable warplane for a very long time. Anyway, all modern military aircraft were made of metal.

The Spanish Civil War, which began in the summer of 1936 and did not end until 1939, although a tragedy for Spain, was a useful proving ground for new weapons and methods for the allies of the respective sides. The tactics appropriate to modern high speed monoplane fighters, explored by the Germans, were not grasped in England until the RAF experienced them at the hands of the Luftwaffe in 1940. On the other hand, the new breed of fast, so-called 'evader' bombers made a distinct impression. In particular, the beautifully sleek Dornier 17s, later to be called the 'Flying Pencil', were so fast that the current crop of Russian and French fighter aircraft could not get near them. The larger Heinkel 111 was not at that time so streamlined, while of course the old boxlike Junkers 52s and Italian tri-motors were unable to run away effectively.

De Havilland were then working on similar lines but in the field of fast civil airliners and wood construction, of which the graceful DH 91 Albatross of 1937 is an example. The fuselage was a strong sandwich of extraordinarily light balsa wood from South America, between layers of pre-formed plywood. The construction of the DH 98, the Mosquito, was to be basically similar.

The effect of giving an aeroplane clean lines was most convincingly demonstrated, to me at any rate, when after flying the Moth biplanes with their struts and wires, I converted to the Miles Magister, a low-wing monoplane. Both carried two passengers, both were powered by the same engine. But the approach to land was quite different. With the Moth you put the nose down to gather speed, and then throttled back, because the machine would then lose speed so quickly. With the Magister, you throttled back, then hauled the nose up so as to lose speed–otherwise the aircraft would fly on interminably before it began to lose height, and it had to have flaps to make it sit down on the grass. The Moths were more fun to fly but aerodynamically they were not in the same class.

On the other hand, the prevailing view at the London Air Ministry favoured the heavily-armed bomber fighting its way through all opposition to the target–and back. When it was tried against the Germans, in 1939, depressingly few returned; but this did not alter the basic Air Ministry view; they just went over to night bombing. These theories explain why the British twin-motor bombers of 1939 all resemble bricks–which you can fly, if you have enough power–because they were armed with power-operated multiple-gun turrets back and front. A splendid idea, had this been 1916. But rifle-calibre machine-guns were now giving way to cannon with long range and heavy punch. By 1940, all British bombers were sitting ducks, in daylight. The Americans, too, began with the idea of the heavily-armed bomber (*really* heavily armed, with half-inch machine-guns instead of .303) battling its way through without fighter escort; and only repeated massacres by the Luftwaffe changed the minds of their Air Generals. But all that was in the future. When the Mosquito was conceived orthodoxy demanded guns, lots of them; even the Germans armed their evader bombers (although not to the high standard of the RAF).

De Havilland began studies for what was to become the Mosquito in the summer of 1938. The basic concept which emerged was for a twin-engined two-seater, totally unarmed, for photo-reconnaissance; a fighter-bomber version which would carry a heavy, fixed forward-firing armament of four cannon and four machine-guns, as well as bombs; and even, as a concession to contemporary thought, a three-man version–the third man being a gunner able to cover the rearward arc. The cost of this third man, and his guns, and his ammunition, and the break in the clean lines caused by a turret, amounted to a ton in weight and a considerable drop in speed. Without a gunner, De Havilland calculated that the Mosquito should be faster than the Spitfire making it virtually uncatchable. Various technical factors were involved, such as higher operating altitude, faired airscrew-blade roots, and the greater smoothness obtained from wood construction–no overlapping plates, no rivets.

Informal discussions went on with Air Marshal Sir Wilfrid Freeman, responsible for development and production at the London Air Ministry, and on 20 September, 1939, Geoffrey de Havilland put on paper the firm's

28

calculations based on a crew of two and two Rolls-Royce Merlin engines–1,500 miles range, two 500 lb or six 250 lb bombs, maximum speed 405 mph at 20,000 feet, cruising speed 320 mph. The letter duly went off to Freeman, but there were sceptics in Air Ministry who considered the data both scanty and optimistic–their calculations gave the Mosquito a top speed of only 250 mph at 18,500 feet. Freeman had few friends at this time.

Nevertheless, the Mosquito became official–that is, an Air Ministry specification was written–on 1 January, 1940. Only four people were present at the meeting: Geoffrey de Havilland, Sir Wilfrid Freeman, John Buchanan (deputy director general of aircraft production) and John Connolly, who at the outbreak of war had been senior engineer of the Air Registration Board. He was to be entirely responsible at the Ministry of Aircraft Production (MAP) for the Mosquito from now until the end of the war. When we met in 1987 Connolly was 80 years old; had been in aviation since 1925, and had even known Orville Wright:

On Day One of the Second World War, as I was on the RAAF reserve of pilots, I was directed to go to Air Ministry and joined John Buchanan, whose boss was Ernest Lemon, a railway engineer who had been appointed to run the Air Ministry Production department. In effect, I was staff officer to Buchanan from September 1939. Under the Ministry dispersal scheme this department moved to Harrogate in Yorkshire in that month.

On 1 January, 1940, Geoffrey de Havilland came up to a meeting with Buchanan, myself and Air Marshal Sir Wilfrid Freeman. Geoffrey de Havilland had with him outline drawings for the Mosquito. He put them on the table, saying: 'This is the fastest bomber in the world; it must be useful.'

We replied: 'You will have no engines, no

aluminium, no undercarriages. 'Geoffrey de Havilland replied that the aircraft was of all-wood construction. Freeman said: 'I am entitled to contract for one or two prototype aircraft, so you go ahead and build it. ' De Havilland replied that that was fine, but he needed a specification. So Buchanan and I there and then wrote a specification (B1/40) for an unarmed bomber, dated that day.

The experimental programme was now official, but there were still no engines for the prototype or a possible companion. The procedure was that Air Ministry supplied the engines, the undercarriages, the instruments and the weapons to the manufacturers of airframes, and they had to be authorised. De Havilland got round one problem by designing and building their own undercarriages, using materials not controlled or in short supply. A strong point made continually by Geoffrey de Havilland was that, while metals and metal workers were at a premium in wartime, there was a good deal of unused capacity in the furniture industry and the wood working trades generally. Another point was that wood lent itself to faster construction–the prototype could be produced within a year. And a final point was that the splendid design staff at De Havilland's were under-employed. The top men could be given the Mosquito.

Leader of the team was Ronald E. Bishop, chief designer, W. A. Tamblin, senior designer, and Richard M. Clarkson, head of aerodynamics. J. A. C. Williams was a senior draughtsman.

For security, both from bombing and from leakage of information, the design team was moved into an historic manor house, Salisbury Hall, which lay behind a moat, surrounded by trees, five miles away from the Hatfield aerodrome and factory. In its grounds a hangar was built to house the prototype Mosquito, and it was constructed to resemble a barn. The previous history of the manor was principally that of discreet country retreat for Charles II and Nell Gwynne, together with their illegitimate offspring, the Duke of St Albans.

It has been suggested that there may have been an extra incentive for the prototype Mosquitos to be tucked away out of sight of Air Ministry officials visiting the main De Havilland complex at Hatfield. There would be no visual cue for any of them to say, 'What! You're not still making that thing, are you? Didn't we cancel it months ago?'

In any event, very soon now the Mosquito was to be stopped, officially at any rate; it could easily have joined the 'might-have-beens' of aviation history.

In the spring and summer of 1940 there was a series of tremendous upheavals. In April, Hitler invaded Denmark and Norway; in May the German army began its blitzkrieg campaign in France; on 4 June the last British troops were evacuated from the sands of Dunkirk; and on 17 June the French government asked for an armistice. British influence on the continent had been totally–and contemptuously–eliminated. As early as May, this deserved calamity resulted in the accession to power of Winston Churchill and his appointment of a Canadian newspaper proprietor, Lord Beaverbrook, to head a Ministry of Aircraft Production.

Lord Beaverbrook decided that production should be concentrated on five types of proven warplane–the Spitfire and Hurricane fighters, the Blenheim light bomber, the Wellington and Whitley medium bombers. The Mosquito was cancelled.

At this time both John Connolly and John Buchanan transferred to Lord Beaverbrook; in June Connolly transferred to Sir Patrick Hennessy (of the Ford Motor Company), the chief executive of the Ministry of Aircraft Production, moving into the old ICI building at Millbank on the Thames, opposite Lambeth Palace. Connolly then became technical adviser to both Hennessy and Beaverbrook and was responsible for the production schedule–

that is, the aircraft programme.

About 1 July, 1940 Geoffrey de Havilland came to see Hennessy and told him: 'I've got the Mosquito builtish.' Wilfrid Freeman had scrounged the two Merlin engines required to power it. Buchanan, Hennessy, Freeman and I all agreed: 'This aircraft is going to be a success.' Geoffrey de Havilland said that the Air Ministry wouldn't give him any orders, so Hennessy said to me, 'What are we going to do about the Mosquito?' I told him that I would talk to Henry Bloss, head of fighter production (DAP1) at MAP. Bloss and I went down to Salisbury Hall, had a look at the prototype Mosquito in a shed, and talked to the chief designer, Bishop, and the head of aerodynamics, Clarkson–both of whom I knew well. Bloss and I went straight back to Hennessy and told him, 'This would be a marvellous aircraft. The Minister (Beaverbrook) should order 50.' After a short argument, the Minister did what we said.

The RAF's aircraft programme for 1940 had contained 37 different types, so Lord Beaverbrook's paring of this to five warplane types is understandable, but hindsight cuts it to two–the Spitfire (except that current production was 'horrendous') and perhaps the Wellington. The Hurricane was greatly inferior, the Blenheim slow as well as being ill-armed, and the Whitley not impressive. Furthermore, as Connolly has pointed out, although engine production at that time was efficient, it was not matched generally by the makers of airframes who were then in a state of 'unplanned chaos'. This, too, had to be sorted out. But the Mosquito was the aircraft of the future–if engines for it could be made available.

When the Minister agreed to give the order for 50 Mosquitos (this was the amount he was allowed to order as an experiment), I wrote the production programme. One Mosquito ordered for November 1940; 49 Mosquitos ordered for December 1940. Ridiculous, of course. The reason was: on that basis, having a contract from the Ministry of Aircraft Production, we could ask Air Ministry for 100 engines. So the Air Ministry was FORCED to give up Merlin engines for the Mosquito–they were in very short supply, being wanted for fighters, etc.

There was no serious experimental flying programme. De Havilland just went ahead with the unarmed bomber. They were remarkably successful. From January 1940 to November 1940, when the prototype flew, with 49 more in the pipeline and the Air Ministry saying, 'We don't want them.'

After those first 50 Mosquitos had been constructed (that is, the materials set aside for them had been used up), De Havilland's said to us (via Lee Murray, the manager at Hatfield):'I want another order for Mosquitos.' So 50 more B1 Bombers were ordered by the Minister, who did what we said, always.

Air Ministry representatives come over from Adastral House once a month to meet the Ministry of Aircraft Production. We had to agree programmes each month. At each meeting the Air Ministry said they didn't want the Mosquito, but I stuck 50 Mosquitos in four times.

Hennessy told me: 'As well as running the programme, you look after the Mosquito,' and from then on, until 1945, I did so. I liaised with all the furniture firms–almost all of them were roped in, perhaps 50 or 60 major firms.

After Geoffrey de Havilland junior had made the first flight of the prototype Mosquito (W4050), he logged 38 hours of test flying in this machine, ironing out various faults–the most serious being tail flutter–before handing it over on 19 February 1941 to the RAF's Aeroplane and Armament Experimental Establishment at Boscombe Down. John Connolly heard that their test pilots did not like the Mosquito's handling characteristics, and certainly there seems to have been an initial reluctance to fly this high-speed wooden aeroplane.

However, tests were eventually carried out (the report runs to many pages) and the top speed was noted as 388 mph at 22,000 feet. There was criticism of the cramped and awkward cockpit layout and the difficulty of getting out of the aircraft–or of anyone getting in to help the crew in the event of a crash. There was trouble with the tail wheel, which would not turn freely, and this caused the fuselage of the prototype to fracture. De Havilland's carried out repairs and the repaired prototype still exists in the museum at Salisbury Hall where the first three prototypes were made. At the same time as the fractured fuselage was rebuilt, the engine's nacelles were extended– and this cured the buffeting. The Boscombe Down test pilots found that this modification stopped the vibration and made the aircraft much pleasanter to fly.

As the Air Ministry were by no means converted to the idea of a fast evader bomber without armament, a Mosquito was fitted with a mock-up of a rearward-firing four-gun turret, which cut the speed by 20 mph. Air Ministry pushed this sort of protection, De Havilland's resisted, and finally the idea was dropped altogether, as the Air Ministry experts gradually came to believe in the Mosquito's claimed performance figures.

As Sir Geoffrey de Havilland pointed out in his autobiography, *Sky Fever,* aircraft speed is difficult to measure accurately, because of possible instrument error or the position of the pitot head. So he borrowed a Spitfire and matched it against a Mosquito. The pilots agreed that the Mosquito was the faster by about 20 mph. It was found also, that when a Mosquito was painted

RAF matt black for night work, there was a noticeable loss of speed. And, further, there were no less than 43 marks of Mosquito, of which 27 were significantly different. The differences included up-rated Merlin engines, too. Anyone desperately seeking the firm ground of figures for Mosquito performance finds himself treading a morass.

However, the results of various tests in 1942 showed that the prototype W4050, re-engined with Merlin 61s for high-altitude work, could reach 40,000 feet, and that other Mosquitos tested with the same engines clocked 413 mph at 17,000 feet and once reached 432 mph. Later in the year, a Mosquito with the even more powerful Merlin 77s, achieved 437 mph at 29,000 feet.

A comparison with contemporary single-engined American fighters showed the Mustang with Merlin 61s achieving 430 mph at 22,000 feet in a Boscombe Down test, and elsewhere a P-47 Thunderbolt reached 416 mph. An unofficial test in 1944 showed that the Mosquito could walk away from the surprised pilot of a twin-engined P-38 Lightning. For some two-and-a-half war years, the only way for a fighter to catch a Mosquito was, with a height advantage, to gain speed by diving on it.

CHAPTER THREE
Arming the Mosquito

I do not know if you are aware of the fact that, at the latter part of the war a 6 lb cannon was fitted to this aircraft and was used with devastating effect.

Letter by E. Field to author, 1987

David King began his career by studying naval architecture, joined the Territorial Army as a Royal Engineer before the war, but when war broke out was working at Vickers Supermarine, Southampton, producing Spitfires–a reserved occupation. Because of North American influence, he was not happy there and in 1940 went as assistant designer to Airspeed's at Portsmouth Airport, some 20 miles away.

I liked that, but in June 1940 I was directed to report to Ronald Bishop, chief designer at De Havilland's, Hatfield. I was early, so on my way I stopped on the North Orbital Road and went into a bar. The radio was on–and on the one o'clock news it was reported that France had capitulated, which dates it. A sinking feeling.

The date was most certainly 17 June for I, too, was in London that day, and bought a paper at lunchtime with the news of the French surrender, noting it in my diary, because at the time it was momentous news. Poland, Holland, Belgium, Denmark, Norway, France–all gone, knocked over like ninepins. Now it was up to us and no one else.

When I arrived at Hatfield, I was taken to Salisbury Hall, a marvellous old moated house. Bishop told me to install four 20 mm cannons and four Browning machine-guns in a Mosquito, as in 1939 I had had experience of fitting 20 mms in the Spitfire.

This armament was not the defensive rearward-firing arrangement originally favoured by the Air Ministry for the bomber version of the Mosquito, but an offensive, forward-firing battery grouped in the nose where De Havilland's had thoughtfully left space under the cockpit flooring. This was similar to the arrangement in the Messerschmitt 110, and was likewise for a twin-engined fighter. The 110 was to fail as a long-range fighter, but proved a useful light bomber during the Battle of Britain (just about to begin) and later as a night fighter, where it was to clash with the DH 98. In versatility, however, the Mosquito was to outdo the Messerschmitt (and indeed all other RAF aircraft): for there were to be bomber, night fighter, high altitude fighter, low altitude intruder, shipping strike, photographic reconnaissance, meteorological and shipborne versions. And that does not exhaust the list.

Pressure was being put on De Havilland's to complete the prototype Night Fighter (W4052) with its armament of 4 x 20 mm Hispano cannon and 4 x . 303 Browning machine-guns, and also the latest airborne radar (AI). There were serious doubts about the 20 mm installation mounted under the nose of the fuselage. The belt feed to the gun which had been fitted to the Beaufighters and Whirlwinds was not considered satisfactory by Squadron Leader 'Dixie' Dean at Boscombe Down. Now it was essential for De Havillands to know quickly what to design for. At the fall of France, Dean had managed to get hold of a French-designed feed called the Chatellerault, which was copied by BSA, and some were made for him. After days and nights of all-out effort he and his team of armourers managed to get it working well enough for him to decide that this was to become the standard feed for all future installations, and the design for W4052 went ahead.

David King was so often at Boscombe Down that he was asked to become a member of the RAF mess there. During this period he was flown down to see an interesting feed then being tested in a Whirlwind prototype; Ron Bishop was the pilot, the plane was a yellow-painted Hornet Moth, and King was only Bishop's second passenger. He put it down in a far corner of the airfield, so that the taxiing time was longer than the flight itself! King duly looked at the Whirlwind and fired the four 20 mm guns. Then they flew back to Hatfield, arriving around 7.30 p.m., and finding that their lateness had created quite a stir. Soon after they had taken off from Boscombe Down, a yellow aircraft was seen to fall in fragments, and it was assumed that this was their Hornet Moth. In fact, it was a Magister trainer downed by a marauding Me 110.

The arrangements for feeding cartridges into the breech of automatic weapons are always likely to go wrong for one reason or another, even in ground guns; but in an aeroplane manoeuvering at high speed, there are in addition 'g' (increased gravity) forces which can affect the usual spring mechanism. This was the initial trouble with the Spitfire's cannon installation, which worked well when in pursuit of lone bombers but in the stress of high-speed dog fighting frequently failed. When this problem was overcome, there arose the question: was the Mosquito's fuselage man enough to take the recoil of a four-cannon battery?

The Ministry gun specialists in the RAF expressed strong views on the wooden structure of the Mosquito being able to stand up to the hammering that the mounting would be required to take from the recoil and return loads from the four cannon, each firing at ten rounds per second. The feed was operated by the recoil of the gun by a finite minimum distance which wound up a clockwork motor in the feed, and this pulled the belted ammo into the breech.

A representative fuselage was built at Salisbury Hall and a complete installation fitted. We had been put in touch with a small, precision engineering firm at Staines called Hydran Products, owned by an extraordinary character called Lew Motley. He had built gun butts in the middle of a field between Staines and Langley, and he quickly fitted the rig in a small open-ended shed. We warned the Ministry and 'Dixie' Dean and a date was fixed for testing. It was mid-January, 1941.

I arrived there soon after dawn and was joined by the Director of Air Armament, Air Commodore A. C. Bilney, and his senior gunnery officer, Wing Commander, 'Dicky' Bird. Within minutes we heard sirens, gunfire, and an aircraft which suddenly broke through the low cloud and was quickly recognised as a Messerschmitt 110. We felt very naked standing around in the snow-covered grass but he flew on. It transpired that he was trying to locate the Hawker aerodrome at Langley.

Very soon after 'Dixie' and an armourer, Corporal Tucker, turned up in an RAF truck, complete with a supply of feeds and boxes of belted rounds. Then R. E. Bishop from De Havilland's arrived, and the trial started. The boxes on the rig were filled (200 rounds per gun), the feeds fitted and the firing mechanism connected. From the gradual build-up of single shots to bursts of increasing length, the only stoppages were caused by feed malfunctions–which were expected in these prototypes which were the only ones available. A careful watch had been kept on the gun mountings and the glued-together structure but no signs of failure had materialised and measurements confirmed that the required recoil distance of the guns, to keep the feeds fully wound, had been maintained.

Feeling very happy, they all gathered at the Woolpack in Staines to celebrate and have lunch. It was then that David King remembered the letter he had just received from Portsmouth, which he had stuffed in his pocket. It was from the firm where he had stored all his and his wife's furniture and personal effects. It said: 'We regret to inform you that during a heavy night raid on the City on the night of 10th Jan 1941, the depository where you stored your effects was completely destroyed by HE and incendiary bombs. While we sympathise with your grievous loss we would like to point out that we too have had many heavy losses. We hope you will be in a position to meet our bill for storage to date, which we enclose.' The bill, for 11 weeks at 7/6, totalled £3. 7s. 0d. It serves now to date approximately the firing tests.

Within a week of the tests we were informed that the Chatellerault feed had been chosen as standard for all future RAF and Naval fighter aircraft. Soon after the three senior trials officers at Boscombe Down were promoted to Wing Commander. They were 'Dixie' Dean–fixed guns; Peter Warwick–gun turrets; Chas. Dann–bombs. 'Dixie' was awarded the AFC–some recognition for the immense responsibilities they bore for the vital importance of the decisions they had to make.

Instrumentation tests on 20 mm Hispano gun

mountings showed that shock loads on firing were completely absorbed in about one-third the distance on wooden structures, compared with metal where breakages were common until new buffering methods were devised. De Havilland's had fortunately found a solution first time. Wooden beams for 20 mm guns of later marks were used on all subsequent aircraft–Hornet, Vampire and the 30 mm Aden guns on the DH 110, later the Sea Vixen, where it was the only wood on an otherwise metal aircraft.

After the fitting of four 20 mm cannon came a tremendous increase in size and hitting power–the installation of a 6-pdr. anti-tank gun in the Mosquito in place of the four 20 mms. The odd origin of this scheme, known as Tsetse, lay in a 1942 suggestion made to a cigarette machine company, Molins, that they produce an automatic feed to the hitherto manually loaded 6-pdr. to be installed in a tank-hunting armoured car. This weird suggestion was totally unsound from a military point of view, and soon dropped, but the work done by Molins on the automatic feed was not wasted. It was to be used first in the Mosquito and then by the motor torpedo boats of Coastal Forces.

Prior to the war, one of Molins' specialities was a machine for weighing cigarettes, which seemed well adapted to handle bullets. There existed a German bullet weighing machine, but it was complicated and hard to maintain, so instead Molins developed their own, which proved to be fast and economical in man hours. Very soon they became expert at producing machinery for arms production. At the time when the 6-pdr. was adapted for the Mosquito, Ted Field was foreman of the welding and fabrication department.

Molins was gifted with a number of very clever

41

designers, some of the best in England. We took a standard 6 lb barrel, such as we used when we designed and made the automatic feed for use in the little ships (MTBs). For the Mosquito, we had to modify the barrel to compensate for recoil. If you look very closely at the pictures on pages 22 and 27 of the company's History, you will notice that we cut the barrel halfway and modified it to counteract shock and recoil.

We then designed, made and fitted a large number of these guns to a standard Mosquito (exact number was a closely guarded secret). As you already know, the Mosquito was one of the most wonderful planes ever made, and with the addition of our gun it became a most terrible and feared weapon. Try and visualise a plane flying at 400 mph, firing a 6 lb shell, and what happened to the target when hit. Even after the end of hostilities very little was broadcast about our gun.

The Mark XVIII Mosquitos carrying the six pounder numbered only 33, and the only unit to receive them was 'C' Flight of 248 Squadron, first in action on 4 November, 1943. But before that, a good deal of ground testing and air firing had taken place. David King of De Havilland's worked with Desmond Molins on this, whom he described as 'a big war winner; modest, charming, very clever'.

I did all the ground firing of the 6-pdr. gun. People didn't believe a wooden framework would stand up to the hammering, but wood absorbs shock loads excellently. The Mark XVIII was armour-plated at the underside of the nose for low level attack. The plate was bolted on and should protect also against muzzle flash and blast from the gun. But we had to find out about gun flash. So, at night, we took the Mosquito to the range, put chocks under it, the photographer set up his machinery, and I got in the cockpit. When I fired the gun there was a 33 feet long flame stabbing into the pitch darkness of the night. Then there was a pounding on the side of the aircraft–a chap trying to tell me that there was a 'bandit' circling overhead! I felt naked sitting there. But they vectored somebody onto it and it went away.

The next stage was a test firing in the air, using solid shot (the normal round for an anti-tank gun designed to pierce armour). It was two o'clock on a brilliantly sunny afternoon when David King took off, with Wing Commander Garland piloting. One reads how, in the Great War of 1914–18, all too often the first plane of a new type loses its way and lands behind enemy lines, an unexpected gift due to too few flying hours by the pilot. It almost happened again in World War Two, with the Mark XVIII Mosquito, but the culprit was the sleepy British weekend.

I was frightened to death over Lyme Bay, feeling that I wouldn't be seeing my wife and kids again. Now the rate of fire was 90 rounds a minute from magazines holding 25 rounds, but for the tests we fired single shots–and there was an awful clanking noise under our feet. I thought the Mosquito was coming apart, but when the pilot asked, 'Are you OK, Dave?' I had to answer 'Yes! 'In fact, the awful noise was just the next round being fed into the breech.

Then the pilot called Boscombe Down for a fix, as usual after air firing finished. He was given it and set that course on his compass. We were over the Channel, out from Lyme Bay in the West Country, and we could make out a distant haze in front of us. Wing Commander Garland then said, 'I can't understand it, the sun is on the wrong side.'

In fact, a sleepy Corporal on weekend duty had given us not the course, but the reciprocal–the haze we saw ahead of us was over the coast of France!

The Wing Commander made a bumpy landing at Boscombe Down (which had an uneven surface), but not until Garland was talking to the Corporal who had given him the wrong course did David realise what had very nearly happened. The West Country tests continued.

At Exeter they had a submarine conning tower rigged up, made of wood. Coming in straight and level at 50 to 100 feet, we could get approximately seven shots in during a mile-long approach: The gun was incredibly accurate–six of the seven shots hit the conning tower.

In the beginning, when Group Captain Reggie Empson came to Bishop and asked if he could put a 6-pdr. gun in a Mosquito, it looked good to us– except for the muzzle blast. Muzzle velocity was 3,400 feet per second. We had borrowed Shrewton Army Tank Training Range for one day, rigged up the 6-pdr, put the Mosquito's tail on a trestle, and I sighted on the target, 25 rounds at 400 yards at a jump card, in bursts of five. The mean point of impact was 10 inches maximum; 200 rounds per gun; 10 seconds' worth.

Wing Commander Rose, who was later lost on a sub-strike, saw a Ju 88 off Lands End and decided to pot it with the 6-pdr. His first shot blew one engine right out of the Ju 88. If the Germans had had a gun as good as that to put in their Ju 88s for attacking massed American formations in daylight, they'd have done greater damage with minimum loss to themselves.

But we only made 33 of these aircraft because the

44

head on the rockets–which was the alternative weapon against submarines and surface ships–had incredibly good underwater characteristics.

The Mosquitos were being improved continually and their armament and carrying capacity being up-rated. For instance, the bomber prototype. W4050, was required to have a bomb bay load of up to 2,000 lbs–with two alternative stowages of either six 250 lb bombs or two 500 lb bombs.

Tim Wilkins, R. E. Bishop's senior assistant– popularly known as 'Wilkie'–saw that if the tail stabiliser of the existing larger bomb could be shortened by a few inches, then four 500 lb bombs could be carried, thus doubling the load. When the Ministry ballisticians were asked if this could be done they were adamant in their refusal. The potential gain in load seemed so attractive that 'Wilkie' set about a bit of tail redesign and this soon resulted in a cylinder fitted with a sleeve which was spring-loaded and activated to slide rearward as the bomb left the bomb bay. Later bombs were short enough to fit without alteration but Wilkie's brain-wave had proved that the Mosquito was capable of carrying the double load.

Later the bomb bay and belly of the bomber Mosquito was altered to take the huge 4,000 lb blast bomb, the 'Cookie'. This variant was developing into a means of delivering a sizeable load, with accuracy, and at high speed, and consequently fewer losses. And when a Mosquito was lost, then only two men were lost with it, not seven, as with the Lancaster, or perhaps even eleven, as with a B-17 Flying Fortress. And, of course, only two Merlin engines were lost, and hardly any metal. Heretics among Mosquito enthusiasts had begun to hint, in whispers, that, given sufficient numbers, the Mosquito could have replaced the lumbering four-engined 'heavies' which suffered so severely in the long nights over Germany.

CHAPTER FOUR
Making the Mosquito

Would it be of interest for you to know that some six million cubic feet of beech trees were felled in the Cirencester Park Woods to be made into plywood at Lydney, Glos for the skins of these aeroplanes? The trees were felled by a New Zealand military forestry company using bulldozers and huge mobile circular saws of a type never seen in this country before.

The Earl Bathurst to the author, 1987

Like the Air Ministry, the War Office and the Ministry of Supply knew exactly what was needed and how it ought to be done. Their current instructions for the extraction of timber as laid down in 1940 read: 'Horse-drawn vehicles only will be used to extract logs from felling sites to sawmills.'

Lt.-Col. G. A. Gamman of the New Zealand Forestry Group of the New Zealand Expeditionary Force read this with incredulity. The expression 'You must be joking' was not then current, but would have expressed his thoughts, as he was to write later.

Our own New Zealand battalion HQ along with 'field' officers had, on board troopships on the way to England, worked out extraction and conversion plans to meet any eventuality under any conditions in which we might find ourselves. If we were to become static, it was agreed in principle that each Company would build and operate four large New Zealand type mills; but not for one moment did we think this static plan would turn out to be our role.

47

When we left our country there was still a 'phoney' war on and Italy had not entered the fray. We sailed from home on 1 May, 1940 (the beginning of the Shooting season in New Zealand) and by the time we arrived on 19 June, Italy was in and Dunkirk was over. It was a strange and unreal sensation to find ourselves sitting on the beaches the day after arrival awaiting the enemy, particularly as all we could muster were 20 rifles and 70 rounds of ammunition.

As events turned out our role was a static one: we moved into Cirencester in August 1940. Our equipment had gone ahead and was lost in France. Four mills per Company strength then. Each mill working an eight-hour shift producing around 1,250 cu. ft of sawn timber per shift: with four mills operational the daily target would be 5,000 cu.ft of sawn timber. (One mill at Overly Woods actually produced 1,646 cu.ft of sawn timber, normal sizes, in 7 hrs 20 mins' cutting time, with a crew of six men.)

Horses were out, so were the two Scottish rack mills already built by the Forestry Commission; neither could possibly have coped with the speed of production. So our private war commenced, particularly with the Director General of the State Forest Service at that time: however, the DG gave way when we convinced him that, apart from power plants and running gear, we could build all our main machinery out of wood; pointing out that this was normal procedure in the industry back home.

He had a final fling, however, when he said to me: 'Well, at least we have chosen good sites for your mill.'

It was with no joy that I told him that the mills were wrongly sited, also.

'Why?' he demanded.

'No water,' I replied.

'What the hell do you want water for?'

'To run on the saws,' I replied.

48

The DG just could not believe his ears. 'Would you like beer instead?' he said.

'I don't mind, if you pay for it to the tune of 500 gallons per day.'

I was becoming a bit cross myself by this time and I retorted: 'Now look here, MATE, if you turn 48-inch diameter circular saws at a thousand rpm spindle speed and feed them at 2½ to 3 inches per revolution and "butt" one flitch after another so that you are cutting timber all day instead of "cutting wind", you are going to have hot saws which will fly to bits unless you run a film of water on the surfaces all the cutting day.'

This DG has long since joined his ancestors; I met him many times during our stay in the Bathurst Park and I don't think he ever quite forgave me for calling him 'Mate'. After all, he was a Knight of the Realm.

It is difficult to realise, when I go past Overley Wood nowadays, that a quarter of a century ago two big, fast cutting mills stood one each end of the 'clearing', just as you leave the forest on the main road to Sapperton; between the two mills were large stacks of timber filling the area; both mills linked with a series of light railways. A memorial in the form of a concrete embankment is still to be seen where logs were rolled off for conversion in one of the mills. These old mill sites hold many memories for me. I recall one beautiful spring morning; the felling gang were sitting in a circle round the log fire having their morning break (smoko). Sitting with them were a few 'timber girls' (land girls) employed for log measuring. In the distance was the spire of the Coates church. This no doubt started the inspiration.

'Pity we have no churches in New Zealand,' said a lumberman.

'Oh, I don't know,' said another.

'What we need are houses,' said the third.

'No houses!' said a land girl.

'No,' said the gang.

'Where do you live, then?' said the land girl.

'In caverns,' came the reply.

'What's a cavern?' said the land girl.

'Cave,' said the gang.

'Good grief!' said the land girl.

And I recall, with some amusement, the very first day the 'axemen' entered the forest at 7.30 a.m. to commence felling operations in Hailey Wood. At 11 a.m. I called at the site, axes, saws and gear everywhere but not a man to be seen anywhere; complete silence. I wandered on, and lo and behold, a 'pub' right in the heart of the forest (Tunnel House)–a bushman's dream come true; even for me. I joined the gang; felling commenced the next day.

We extracted approximately six million cubic feet from the three forests in three years. It was necessary to go through the forests three times. As the demand for timber increased the quarter girth was lowered: this, along with the fact that I could not spare expert men to clear up as they worked, left a dreadful mess when we pulled out. When I reflect on those days I recall that the big contractors who today build motorways and the like with the most modern machinery, came to me to borrow my bulldozer drivers to teach their men how to use crawler tractors and bulldozers. This kind of machinery was almost unheard of back in 1940.

It was not all that easy to command troops who, through their job of work, became part of the local scene–they 'get their feet under the table'. However, these New Zealand sappers were men of remarkable quality both physically and mentally. Men from the mountains and forests–the Company strength 200; average height six feet; average weight 13 stone

10 lbs. They made many friends in Cirencester and even to this day–30 years later–some of the residents of this town still correspond with those old soldiers.

From acting the most reluctant bride the Air Ministry became the urgently imploring suitor. They wanted Mosquitos–lots of them. But they dithered as to what sort of Mosquitos they wanted and in what numbers. There were then three basic prototypes–for the unarmed bomber, for the radar-equipped night-fighter, and for the high-flying long-range photo reconnaissance version packed with cameras. First the Air Ministry wanted all one lot, then half-a-dozen of one and six of the other, metaphorically speaking, for they changed their minds so many times it would be tedious to list their constantly changing proportions. And the aircraft were not the same, not interchangeable. The fighter version, for instance, had to be stronger built–more highly stressed–in order to be violently thrown about in combat. And the very high-flying version had to have a pressurised cabin.

From the beginning De Havilland had planned to sub-contract, so as to avoid the wholesale layoffs of staff which had occurred after the 1914-18 war. But this had meant telling potential sub-contractors that, any minute now, vast orders for the Mosquito would be given. In wartime, it was not possible to mount a publicity campaign about a secret aeroplane, but De Havilland did the next best thing–arranged demonstrations at Hatfield for the great and influential. Geoffrey de Havilland had worked up a truly spectacular routine, screaming across the aerodrome at 400 mph on two engines before doing a series of upward rolls on one engine. Many aircraft at the time could barely maintain height on half power, let alone do climbing aerobatics. Knowledgeable peoples' eyes popped out.

The first demonstration took place on 29 December, 1940, one of the VIPs being Canada's Minister of

Munitions and Supply, C. D. Howe. The Minister had experienced the realities of World War Two 15 days before, when he had been rescued in mid-Atlantic from the torpedoed *Western Prince*. As in the Great War, it was the U-Boat which was to prove the greatest threat to Britain, and an aircraft the submarine's worst enemy. On 26 April, 1941, the VIPs at the demonstration included Lord Beaverbrook and the US Air General Arnold. A cunning gambit had been to programme immediately before the Mosquito a plodding procession of American lease-lend aircraft.

The *De Havilland Gazette* of September 1945 was to recall the urgency of 1941:

> The drive to increase and expand went out like a great crusade, carried into the byways by teams of car-driving contact men who, despite fires, blast and craters, poor tyres and petrol coupons, struggled to build up the output from hundreds of suppliers. . . Everyone worked very long hours. It gives some idea of the pressure all round the organisation to mention that there were 10,000 drawings and schedules for the Mosquito, against 1,400 for the Tiger Moth.

And, of course, De Havilland still had to turn out Tiger Moth and Oxford trainers, as until now these had been regarded by the Air Ministry as being of real importance to the war, unlike the unbelievable DH 98. There were many, many hundreds of sub-contractors, large and small, and sub-sub-contractors. One of the smallest was located in a family house in Surbiton, London. Michael S. Gampell recalled:

> In 1940, my parents (both now dead) sent us three children off to Canada, while they stayed put in Surbiton to fight the war. My father was with

Reuter's, but my mother, finding herself with a large, empty house, decided that there was a worthwhile role in turning the drawing-room into a factory, using local half-day volunteer (but paid) workers.

It took her two years to get any part of the government even to consider the idea, but in 1942 the Ministry of Aircraft Production gave her the chance to try. The first (and only) contract was to cut, tag and braid (and later to tropicalise) the cockpit intercom cords for the Mosquito, as sub-contractors to LPE. From 1942, right through to the end of the war, 20 women in the morning, and a different 20 in the afternoon, sat at worktables and got on with the job. My mother used to say they ranged from duchesses to charladies. I believe that 100 per cent of the Mosquito intercom cords passed through the house. Her idea mushroomed, and there were similar units all over the country, but ours, and the Mosquito, was the first.

I suppose you will be concentrating on the fighting and reconnaissance roles of that marvellous ply-wood aircraft, rather than the odd, determined bunch who actually got them built, but you might just find space to mention them.

W. J. Ince, who had left the 94 Shop at Hatfield ten minutes before the bombs demolished it and much of the material stored for the building of Mosquitos, recalled:

I was in the Electrical section, then the experimental department at Salisbury Hall, where there were lots of mods to do. I installed the electrics in the cockpit and for the cameras, and so on. The first batches made at Chester were not up to scratch and we had to work every night, and were called 'Ghosters'. For instance, on Monday a plane from Chester might come in. If so, we'd clock on at 8 a.m. and work all night, then next day, then part of the night to perhaps two in the morning, just to get the plane ready, ripping out the electrical boxes and wiring first. The usual weekday was 8 a.m. to 8 p.m., but only 8 to 5 on Saturdays and Sundays. Perhaps 100 hours a week. One week, I took just half-an-hour off to go out and have breakfast, and when I got back, they thought I was late!

I remember the last Mosquito which came along the track. Lots of us painted our initials on it. The Mosquito was a wonderful thing. We also worked on Hurricanes, which took a long time to repair, being metal (usually damaged around the cockpit). But a Mossie was quick. If a wing was damaged, just saw off that wingtip and scarf a new one on. In in the morning, out the same evening!

As a young draughtsman, A. E. Hurren worked on the Mosquito aeroplane for nearly three years in the experimental drawing office of De Havilland's factory at Hatfield.

Before joining De Havilland's in August 1942, I was a draughtsman in the Royal Air Force, stationed at No. 13 MU (Maintenance Unit) at Henlow in Bedfordshire. Due to the need for skilled draughtsmen in the Aircraft industry at that time, however, I responded to a short-term release scheme set up by the Air Ministry and was directed to a special-purpose employment centre in London where Chief Draughtsmen and Personnel Managers from various aircraft companies were conducting interviews. The particular employer I met was a Mr Percy Brian who was De Havilland's Chief Draughtsman.

After a short discussion on the work involved and my previous experience, I was offered an appointment on a six-month release basis for the princely sum of three pounds per week! Although this was more than double my RAF pay, my clothes, meals, living accommodation and travelling fares took a large proportion of this salary! However, I accepted the job and subsequently made my way to Hatfield where I sought digs and swapped my uniform (pro-tem) for civilian clothes. As it turned out, I never wore my uniform again because the six-month release period was continually extended until my eventual demobilisation in 1946.

I went to work in the Experimental Department. This was a large complex fronted by a long, two-storey brick building which housed the Design Office downstairs and the Drawing Offices upstairs.

At the rear of this complex, there were workshops and hangars, as well as the Lofting Office. This was a very large room where various pieces of the aircraft were drawn full-size onto aluminium alloy metal sheets which were usually a standard size of eight feet by four feet and about 3 mm thick. These sheets lay flat upon an expanse of low tables about three foot or so high, and upon which draughtsmen and draughtswomen wheeled themselves into position by kneeling on little trolleys or just working on their knees.

Generally, the draughtsmen schemed out the various configurations of the aircraft geometry in hard pencil, and the draughtswomen finalised the required outline shapes in indian ink. This was a dense, black waterproof fluid which caused messy problems and great dismay to all concerned when accidentally spilled! On the few occasions when I went into the Lofting Office, I always reflected that although I enjoyed practically all the professional applications of engineering drafting, this particular branch had never appealed to me in the slightest and I was glad that I had never been called upon to become involved in this very exacting and strenuous side of draughtsmanship. But I greatly admired the immense patience and dedication of those who did this work.

Probably the most important of all the experimental department work-shops was the place where the 'mock-up' of the Mosquito was constructed. This 'mock-up' was in fact a full-size wooden model of the aircraft on which shape, calculations and dimensions could be verified, as well as the location, access and functioning of components, armament and other equipment on a development and assessment basis. Designers, draughtsmen and technicians were continually using this most valuable means of witnessing the effects of their individual and combined efforts to achieve the aircraft design specifications set by the Air Ministry and the Design management of the De Havilland Company.

The particular nature of the work assigned to me on the Mosquito was extremely varied and involved nearly every stage of fabrication and assembly. It demanded the utmost attention to detail at all times, cheerful perseverance and the ability to get along with other people. Basically, I had to progress and incorporate some of the hundreds of variations and modifications that were initiated by the company's Inspection Department, and arose from the many day-to-day queries met during construction. Despite the care and thought involved during design and detailing on the drawing board, and also the trial fitting carried out on the 'mock-up' and the prototype aircraft, there were always unforeseen and unpredictable problems encountered on the production aircraft. There were also many improvements found from experience and the variation in the particular type or 'mark' of Mosquito being made.

Any alteration, improvement or error, irrespective of magnitude, was generally recorded in the form of a single-sheet report, describing in simply written detail, usually with thumbnail sketches, the precise need for modification or incorporation to the aircraft's build specification.

This particular form was called a 'Works Query Note' and usually required the authorisation of the Aircraft Inspection Department before it was sent to the Drawing Office for examination and processing. Whether it was an alteration due to a drawing dimension error, an incorrect bolt size, a malfunction problem on the undercarriage, an updated paint specification number or the reinforcement of a structural member, it invariably meant that the draughtsman concerned had to leave his drawing board in order to visit the particular workplace and witness the problem first hand.

The tendency to avoid this exercise was always tempting, particularly when the particular query to be investigated was in a hangar possibly half a mile away from the Drawing Office, and when it was teeming with rain or bitterly cold. A telephone call was sometimes an alternative, but one could never be certain that verbal communication and descriptions were mutually accurate or that transmitter and receiver really understood or appreciated the crux of the problem.

Therefore these matters were usually discussed with the AID (Aircraft Inspection Department) Inspector and other associated technical personnel, to ensure that the desired modification or course of action would best solve the problem with the utmost regard for safety and economy, and would be carried out in the quickest possible time.

Having gleaned all the facts, the draughtsman would then return to his drawing board and proceed to obtain all the relevant drawings and schedule lists that would need to be modified and amended. Sometimes this involved the alteration of as many as twenty or thirty separate drawings, as well as the preparation of new drawings when different or additional components were required to be made.

Schedules were in effect a shopping list of all the components concerned on a particular assembly or sub-assembly in itemised form, giving part numbers and description, etc. These also needed changing and bringing up to date in line with the various alterations. Sometimes a standard component used on the Mosquito was also used on other aircraft made by the company, like the Tiger Moth trainer aeroplane, for instance. It was then essential to ensure that any alteration was acceptable to both aircraft and that an increase in number off was recorded in the shopping list or schedule.

To assist in the procurement of the relevant original drawings from the drawings library, the services of drawings librarians were essential. When one considers that an aircraft like the Mosquito involved the preparation of something in the order of thirty thousand drawings, the chore of information retrieval, as it was then in 1942, required regulated filing systems and storage so that every original drawing was accounted for and could be located and produced quickly. There were no computer programs to search and find: only people with active and retentive minds–and matching strong limbs to fetch and carry piles of drawings! Only the drawings librarians were therefore allowed anywhere near the drawing cabinets, in order to prevent the chaos that could ensue if all drafting personnel were allowed to help themselves to drawings.

It was during one of my countless visits to the assembly line that I was most intrigued to see several midgets walking into the factory. This puzzled me for some time but I was told that these little people were actively engaged in a very important capacity on the Mosquito assembly line, one that only they could adequately perform with maximum efficiency. Their task, apparently, was to go inside the smallest section of the fuselage, at the tail end, to establish that the two halves of the fuselage were securely glued together and that the requisite fittings at that end of the aircraft were to specification. To explain here, the Mosquito was made mainly of wood: fuselage, wings, tailplane and control surfaces were all constructed in wood. The fuselage in particular was made of a kind of wooden sandwich about 16 mm thick, with the 'bread' being 2 mm plywood and the 'meat' being solid balsawood–the same balsa material, in fact, that boys of all ages have used, and are still using, to make model aeroplanes. The exception, however, was the glue. It was not the usual balsawood cement but a new kind of two-part adhesive 'Beetle' glue. This comprised a mauve-coloured hardener which, when mixed with a basic glue body, produced a time-dependent cement which had immense strength.

I was informed subsequently, however, that when the Mosquito was in service operations in the far east, this cement proved not to be resistant to the appetite of the white ant. Apparently on a number of Mosquitos, some of the wooden sandwich panels on the fuselage and other parts of the aircraft were found to be springing into an undignified self-unpeeling function when they were dispersed close to camouflage foliage and subjected to humid and damp atmospheres, as well as the hunting grounds of these scavenging ants.

To return to the completed pile of modified drawings and schedules: these were all original documents. That is to say, they were the actual sheets of paper that the draughtsman or technical clerk had compiled. These never left the offices. They were, however, drawn on transparent or tracing paper and could therefore be duplicated by taking prints of them onto sensitised paper–much the same as a photograph but on a much larger scale, using a dyeline process. Sometimes an ammonia process was used, causing one's eyes to water when one had to check through a batch of drawings before the ammonia fumes had time to evaporate. Because of the many departments within the Hatfield factory that needed to have copies of these prints in order to carry out the required alterations, as well as the many sub-contractors in other parts of the country, a considerable number of prints had to be produced. I can recall that as many as thirty copies of all drawings and schedule lists were needed.

When one considers that some extensive modifications involved possibly twenty or more drawings and schedules, this meant that about six hundred prints had to be produced and distributed. Furthermore, because the drawings had been updated, the existing drawings owned by all concerned were now obsolete and had to be collected and destroyed to ensure that everyone was working to the latest information. Usually the obsolete prints were torn into small sheets and the back of them used for scrap paper: so there was some recycling to absorb a portion of the expense of these ongoing alterations and amendments.

On the list of departments to get up-to-date drawings was the technical illustrations drafting office. Here worked some extremely talented graphic illustrators, able to draw quickly and skilfully fascinating cut-away sections of the aircraft in precise perspective, from simple 3D views of a small assembly to a deep section into the entire innards of the Rolls Royce 'Merlin' engines that powered the Mosquito. These were used for handbooks, training and service manuals, etc. It was always a wonderland in this small but industrious office, and it was there that I first met one of the senior illustrating draughtsmen, David Kossof. We met often in the train during our daily travels between King's Cross and Hatfield, and I used to assist him at times when he was learning his scripts for his early theatrical work. Little did he or I know then that he was to become such a successful and well known character actor. I remember him telling me that he had come to De Havilland's from one of the major London furniture manufacturing companies where he was a furniture designer.

Many well known furniture companies, such as Harris Lebus, E. Gomme Ltd and Dancer and Hearne Ltd., were involved with the construction of the Mosquito which, being an all-wood aircraft, needed the expertise of the skilled woodworkers employed by these companies. The beech, birch, spruce and balsa woods used for the aircraft were not as exotic as the mahogany, walnut and maple used for the furniture, but they all needed expert and accurate handling. There were no decorative applications for the warplane, only strength and shape. Such was the accuracy of woodworking at De Havilland's that the general workshop tolerances were in the order of plus or minus one ten thousandth of an inch (0.010″, or a quarter of a millimetre in metric terms)!

During those wartime days we all learnt a great deal about each other's skills and how to appreciate their application to such a wonderful aeroplane as the Mosquito. One can never explain to the non-aircraft employee the special pride and possessive thrill of being on the tarmac to watch a Mosquito swooping in high-speed flight from out of the clouds above and across the airfield with the magnificent roar of full power, nearly touching the grass and then back up into the clouds again. Even though my contribution was confined mainly to alterations and amendments in the early days, I always felt very proud, and still am, to have helped the Mosquito to fly.

Although the Mosquito lacked solidity, unlike, say, the hull of a wooden ship, ingenious diagonal overlapping of the plywood sandwich made for a strong structure. Of course, jokes about a wooden aeroplane in 1940 were legion. One critic called it a 'tea chest'. One joker, on learning that among the furniture firms employed as sub-contractors for the Mosquito was a maker of coffins, suggested that all it needed to complete an operational Mosquito was to add a pair of handles. 'Flying Furniture' was another nickname, but probably the best known comment was that if a Mosquito fell apart in the air, then the aerodrome would be littered with matchsticks and copies of the *Daily Mirror*.

Those were jokes. The reality could be horrifying. Leslie E. Veit, then with an Air Transport Squadron of the USAAF, saw the break-up of what was probably a Canadian-built Mosquito.

Please forgive an old man if I can't remember dates too well, but the facts are very vivid to this day. It was early September 1944, and we were flying to the UK, as we called it then. We were in C-47s (Dakota to you) and we made it in many short hops because of range.

We had landed at Goose Bay, Labrador, on a beautiful day and the next morning were held up by weather in Iceland. Since the plane had 20 hours on

62

it I decided to pull a 25-hour inspection, thus getting to know my new plane better, and being sure everything was set for our long overwater flight. As I worked on my Goony Bird I kept hearing a strange looking plane making passes of the field.

The roar of engines really got my attention as this plane made a low pass along the runway, pulling up into a near vertical climb as it passed me. Suddenly there was a booming noise and the plane just disintegrated in flight. The largest pieces to come down were the engines. I spotted one parachute. As I watched spellbound, I realised the man in the chute was hanging head down. His feet were tangled in the shroud lines, and he was heading for the concrete runway. Running as fast as I could, as I wanted to break his fall, I was too late. Luckily for him the wind carried him off the runway. He landed head first in loose sand about six or eight feet off the concrete, about 20 yards from me. As the meat wagon was very close by at that moment, and not wanting to compound any injuries, I did not touch him.

I returned to my plane and for the next five or ten minutes it rained pieces of balsa and spruce veneer like the autumn leaves. I heard later, that this plane had a vibration problem and that an RAF pilot and a De Havilland man were on board. When we finally took off the next day the other one had not been found. I am sorry to tell you so sad a tale about your beautiful Mosquito, but felt you should know.

De Havilland had formed subsidiary companies in Canada and Australia. De Havilland Canada had been in existence as far back as 1928, building variants of the Moth, often modified to suit local conditions. When war broke out in Europe, both were primarily engaged in building trainers. In 1940 De Havilland Canada received an influx of talent from Poland, the most prominent of whom was Wsiewolod J. Jakimiuk, former chief engineer of the National Aircraft Factory in Warsaw. A great number of Mosquitos were to be made in Canada and a fair number in Australia; there was at this time even a possibility that the Mosquito would be built in America, as a result of General Arnold's report on the April 1941 demonstration at Hatfield. But five American companies were asked to evaluate the data he had brought to the USA from De Havilland's–Fleetwings, Beech, Hughes, Fairchild and Curtiss-Wright. The report from Beech summed up their views:

> It appears as though this airplane has sacrificed serviceability, structural strength, ease of construction and flying characteristics in an attempt to use construction material which is not suitable for the manufacture of efficient airplanes.

This contemptuous dismissal proved a blessing in disguise. De Havilland expertise was being spread thin as it was, with a new shadow factory and countless subcontractors in England, plus both Canadian and Australian works to be guided into the production of the new warplane. There was a bright side to North American negotiations. Packard agreed to build the Rolls Royce Merlin engine, which the Americans needed to power their own P-51 Mustang, and would supply the same engines to De Havilland Canada for installation in their Mosquitos.

In July 1941 Lee Murray, general manager at Hatfield, arrived in Canada to study the potential there; this visit resulted in a MAP order for De Havilland Canada to build 400 Mosquito bombers powered by the Packard-built Merlin 31. Ten days after this had been announced, two more senior Hatfield men arrived–W. D. Hunter and Harry Povey.

64

Their arrival coincided with grim days in the Atlantic. A mild foretaste was the loss, on the first shipment, of two per cent of the key Mosquito drawings. A complete Mosquito shipped in flyable condition arrived, due to rough handling, in need of extensive repair; castings suffered salt corrosion; but many assemblies and drawings never did arrive, sunk by the 'Wolf Packs' running loose among the convoys in the mid-Atlantic gap where no air cover could be given, at that time. On two later occasions drawings covering variant changes went down with their ships, as did vital hydraulic assemblies.

In the spring of 1942 De Havilland Canada received a contract for 1,100 Mosquitos financed by United States Lend Lease, in addition to the 400 already ordered. From a high American source now came glowing reports on the worth of the Mosquito for photo-reconnaissance. The source was Colonel Elliot Roosevelt, son of the President, who was flying a British Mosquito IV in the North African campaign. The idea of a twin-engined fighter was also catching on. And just at this time production was not flowing as it should. The Company was now largely financed and virtually owned by the Canadian government in Ottawa; and a good deal of swift knife-work took place, the pros and cons of which would now be hard to establish. The situation was not eased by more of those policy changes to which De Havilland Hatfield had long been accustomed. First, only the Mark XXVI Bomber (the 'XX' designated a Canadian-built machine) was to be made; then the FB Mark XXI fighter bomber was to be constructed as well; and after that the dual-control trainer was added; and as a further complication, the conversion of Mosquitos for the USAAF photo-reconnaissance units, which bore the 'star and bar' instead of roundels and the American designation F-8.

There were differences, too, between English and North American practices in engineering and manufacture; and differing opinions also. Harry Povey had been brought up in the English tradition of wooden jigs; some of the Canadians preferred metal jigs. And around this time Canadian-built Mosquitos, once production speeded up, were acquiring a bad reputation on the airfields of Europe and the Far East. One reason was the humidity of Toronto, the home of De Havilland Canada, which was on the Great Lakes. The wooden jigs to make the fuselage varied very much. Mosquitos did not come out the right size. John Connolly and Harry Povey were to solve this problem.

The half-shells of the fuselage were made of sandwiches of plywood and balsa wrapped around a wooden pattern and held down by metal straps. It was desirable to heat the glue to set it fast. This, and moisture from the glue in the Canadian climate, caused the 40 feet long wooden mould to vary.

Povey suggested concrete. I had been a concrete engineer and I designed the process to cast concrete accurate to 1/10th inch from a plaster 'female' mould which also had to be accurate, as it was taken from the Master wooden mould at De Havilland's.

This was a highly technical problem of 'know-how' about shrinkages of large plaster casts as well as the same phenomenon of reinforced concrete. It was in the Harris Lebus factory at Tottenham in London that I made the moulds and eventually used either 'microwaves' or heated straps to set the glue. I don't think this process has ever been written about. We should have taken out a patent!–as it resulted in the microwave oven of today. . .

In the summer of 1943 the first five Mosquitos destined for the RAF flew the Atlantic, using giant 200-gallon fuel tanks, designed by W. J. Jakimiuk to fit into their bomb bays. In the summer of 1944 regular deliveries began, using the northern route, but as winter came on engine failures were reported, some of them due merely to the oil gauges giving false readings, leading to an unnecessary shutdown of the engine. If it was the right-hand engine, which was the sole source of generator power, then the radio failed, too. On 12 November a Mosquito disappeared having sent an SOS but not stating what the trouble was. On 30 November another Mosquito vanished, this time without a message and without trace. It was decided that winter weather must be the cause, and the trans-Atlantic flights were switched to the warmer southern route. 22 Mosquitos were sent off on 15 December, 1944, flown by experienced crews and in good weather;. and two more disappeared. Then another two had to make emergency landings due to one engine failing. All Mosquitos were grounded.

All possible snags were investigated, including a build-up of an explosive mixture of petrol fumes in the cockpit due to a badly-sited venting tube. Also, better exhaust pipes were fitted and five hours additional flight testing ordered. Not all pilots were convinced that the answers had been found.

Just before Christmas 1944, a Mosquito crew on a test flight reported a jammed aileron, were given permission to jump, but preferred to try a landing; both were killed. But the wreckage was there to inspect. The cause had been bad workmanship and sloppy inspection. A wooden plug covering an inspection opening lacked a retaining screw; the vibration in flight had brought the plug out of position and it had jammed the aileron. A small, simple fault–but deadly.

The probable solution to some of the mysterious disappearances on the Atlantic ferry route was obtained by Jim Henderson in March 1945, by which time the war in Europe was almost over. He was one of 23 Mosquito crews waiting at Gander to continue to the Azores when the weather improved; a succession of 'fronts' had kept them waiting for ten days. At the first sign of clearance, the Air Force crews were ordered off, and had no option but to go; the civilian crews, with equal misgivings, had the option of refusal. However, both Henderson and Woodrow Walden, flying another Mosquito, were employees of De Havilland Canada, and felt they had to go, despite hot opposition from some of the others. In all, only six Mosquitos took off.

Henderson and Walden had agreed to take off together and keep in radio contact, but Walden had minor engine trouble and was delayed ten minutes; they never did make radio contact, and Walden's aircraft vanished. Some of the six got through, while others turned back, but what happened to Henderson seemed explanation enough. The take-off was made in clear weather but an hour later they found themselves flying in haze at 15,000 feet. After two hours 20 minutes, they heard a weather alert broadcast from Gander. Henderson tried to climb above the weather, but at 23,000 feet was still inside cloud. He noticed the ominous, shiny glint of ice forming on the wings, and decided to turn back. As he took the plane into a slow turn the Mosquito stalled and dived to 10,000 feet before Henderson could regain control. Walden, whose first Atlantic crossing this would have been, probably fell victim to the Mosquito's lack of de-icing gear.

In June 1944, a mechanised assembly line had been introduced at De Havilland Canada. It occupied two large assembly bays some 600 feet long and 130 feet wide. By 1945 the number of assembled fuselages had outstripped demand and the surplus were stacked in a far corner of the hangar until needed. As it turned out, for a time other, more pressing needs were catered for by a brilliant female entrepreneur. A completed fuselage offered the necesary privacy for her trade (reputedly the world's oldest). When word went round that it was 'the second fuselage from the end', a brisk trade ensued. But it was short-lived.

Equally short-lived were various ruses to smuggle Company (now Canadian government) equipment out of the plant. One of the most ingenious and carefully prepared efforts became known as the 'turkey raffle caper'. The worker concerned appeared at the security gates with a parcel from which dangled two turkey legs; the man seemed overjoyed at having won his department's Christmas Turkey raffle. No one suspected that the parcel might be a trifle heavy, until the wrappings tore and a ten-pound vice thumped to the ground at the security guard's feet.

In all, more than 7,700 Mosquitos were built in Britain, Canada and Australia.

CHAPTER FIVE
They Led the Way
(1941-1942)

On 3 October, 1940, I was being driven from Salisbury Hall
to the factory at Hatfield when it was bombed by a single Ju
88. I stopped in a lane a mile away, and can recall the smoke,
the noise, and that I was frightened. But we learned about
'Skip Bombing' from that.

David King to the author, 1987

Although the Mosquito had been conceived primarily as
an evader bomber, the first into action by a long way
were unarmed, camera-equipped machines of No. 1
Photographic Reconnaissance Unit from Benson,
Oxfordshire. On 17 September, 1941, S/Ldr Rupert
Clerke took off to photograph naval targets in France–
Brest, Bordeaux and La Pallice–and then to check the
Spanish-French frontier for possible German troop movements. From 24,000 feet the Mosquito did the job–but the
cameras did not. An electrical fault resulted in blank
film. From a still-suspect, generally unwanted aircraft,
this was not an auspicious debut.

More than half a year elapsed before the first Mosquito
night-fighters took off on an operation. On 14 April,
1942, 47 German raiders bombed Norwich by night. The
first Mosquito airborne got two radar contacts–both of
them British. The next Mosquito away briefly obtained a
contact–and then lost it. The third Mosquito had no
success at all.

The first Mosquito bombers took off for Germany the
following month–all four of them. On the night of 30/31
May, 1942, Air Marshal Harris staged the first 'Thousand

Bomber Raid' on Cologne by putting up everything which would fly, including training machines with trainee crews. As this monstrous gaggle were returning, the four Mosquitos from 105 Squadron—the first to be given a few Mosquitos—were sent off at intervals. The last three of the four found Cologne obscured by a vast pall of smoke, so bombed into the murk on dead reckoning. In daylight on the 31st, another Mosquito went out to photograph the damage, broke out of cloud 60 miles from Cologne and reached the city flying at high speed at low level. The pilot, S/Ldr Channer, reported that no one knew he was there until he was gone. He went slap over a marshalling yard—no one looked up. Cattle in the fields took no notice of the aeroplane. At Mosquito speed, the sound of the engines was travelling with a time-lag behind the aircraft. Channer believed that the correct way to employ Mosquitos was against carefully selected targets, for maximum hurt with minimum effort. This was at that time impossible for the main force, which could aim only at cities; and not infrequently were five to ten miles inaccurate in their aim.

During this year, 1942, De Havilland's produced within one week a very high-flying Mosquito in an endeavour to catch the Junkers 86Ps which were coming over at a great height (sometimes at more than 40,000 feet) and dropping a few small bombs as well as taking photographs. The Spitfires failed to catch them, but it was thought Mosquitos might. So a lot of effort was diverted from an aircraft which promised exceedingly well at low level to a version which would fly at the heights you and I are accustomed to when being package-toured to Italy or Greece, but which were amazing in the light of 1942 technology. Then the Germans, surly and unco-operative as usual, discontinued their overflights with the Junkers 86P—and so removed the target.

Two years earlier, in 1940, the Mosquito had been a secret held under round-the-clock guard. When, in May

1941, a German spy had been caught near Salisbury Hall, there were suspicions that his target might have been the secret bomber. He was an SS Officer, Karel Richard Richter, who had been dropped by parachute with a radio transmitter; but he was caught within 20 minutes of venturing out onto a public road; and cannot have co-operated, for he was executed in December 1941.

In September 1942, the Mosquito ceased to be a secret. After a display in Canada of the aeroplane's capabilities, the station newspaper of 5 SFTS reported both the demonstration and the fact that the machine was being manufactured in Canada—much to the fury of the rest of the media, who had been cheated of a scoop by the littlest of little brothers. After much futile fuming and recrimination, an Official World Press Release was made on 26 September, 1942. On 27 October, the *Daily Express* ran a two-page spread under the headline SWIFTEST BOMBER—FROM WOODSHOP, telling how a firm which had formerly made 'bookcases and bedroom suites' was now making the fastest warplane in the world. And the report listed three main roles: Long-range day bomber; Long-range fighter-bomber or escort bomber; Long-range picture-gathering reconnaissance machine. The dimensions were given but, naturally, not the performance figures. More technical articles appeared in *The Aeroplane* of 15 January, 1943, *Flight* of 6 May, 1943, and *Aircraft Production* for June 1943.

One of the early enthusiasts for the Mosquito was Captain R. Levy, DFC, who has just retired as an airline pilot and now lives in Belgium.

Although living in Lancashire most of my youth, I was actually born in Portsmouth. Early in 1942 I came back from my training in the USA with the first class of UK cadets (42A) trained under the 'Arnold Scheme'. As a young sergeant pilot with 200 hours (an enormous figure by the standards of the

72

day), I was sent to 17 Operational Training Unit for conversion to Blenheims. My instructor had 65 hours! One day we were at dispersal when the aerodrome was well and truly 'beaten up' by an aeroplane the like of which we had never seen before. It finished the 'beat up' by feathering an engine, and departed in an upward roll. It was June 1942 and this was my first sight of the Mosquito; from then on there was no other aeroplane for me.

I was fortunate enough to be one of the two crews selected to be posted to the very first Mosquito squadron, No. 105, then stationed at Horsham St Faith near Norwich. No. 105 was commanded by the legendary Hugh Idwal Edwards, VC, and every other decoration possible. They had just converted from Blenheims and had suffered from murderous losses from both the enemy and from the aircraft itself, which, once you were able to get into the cockpit, was the worst that I had ever encountered. You were just as likely to pull a fuel-cock lever shut after take-off as to change the two-pitch prop to fine pitch.

The names and the people themselves on the Squadron were very over-awing to a young sergeant pilot. S/Ldr Parry, Dixie Dean, Tommy Browne and the incredible team of Roy Ralston with his navigator, Syd Clayton. They had made over 100 sorties on Blenheims and Mosquitos, including bombing a train going into a tunnel and then nipping round to the other side and neatly sealing it off with another bomb. When they tried to 'screen' Syd Clayton after his 100th 'op', he talked the RAF into sending him to Canada, where he gained his wings as a pilot, and came back and flew–Mosquitos!

Flying took on a new aspect with 105 Squadron. Practice low flying at rooftop height, roaring over the farms, houses and fields of East Anglia. Practice 'bounce or skip' bombing with 11½ lb practice bombs; and all complaints dealt with by our Station Commander, 'Groupie' Kyle, now Air Marshal Sir Wallace Kyle.

The bomb load we carried was 4 x 500 lbs. The bombs had been specially modified with short fins to fit into the Mosquito bomb-bay, with the result that the two-man crewed wooden Mosquito carried the same load–2,000 lbs–as the eleven-man crewed B-17 Flying Fortress and could carry it to Berlin without fighter escort.

Indeed, we had no armament, relying on speed and hedge-hopping tactics. At that time the Focke-Wulf 190 was appearing and they could get in one attack on us if they saw us first. The main casualties came from flying into the ground or sea, bird-strikes, and even from our own bombs. These were fitted with an 11-seconds delay but sometimes this didn't work or else you were unlucky enough to get the blast from someone else's bomb. I remember watching with apprehension a bomb, from the machine in front of me, bounce high over my wing whilst attacking the marshalling yards at Terquier, France, on 3 January, 1943.

Just before that, on New Year's Eve, 1942, I had been on another marshalling yard attack to Mouceau-sur-Chambres in Belgium. It was dusk and we ran into a snow storm, and I flew between two huge slag heaps, only seeing them as they flashed past high above each wing. We then hit a bird which smashed through the windscreen, covering my observer, Les Hogan, and myself with feathers and blood. It was bitterly cold all the way back and although we bathed, scrubbed and scrubbed again the bird smell hung around and we were not the most popular partners at the New Year's Eve dance.

74

It was during this period that 105 Squadron, with its sister Squadron 139, made some of the most spectacular and daring raids of the war. They heartened a British nation still despondent from the Blitz and the setbacks in the Atlantic and the Far East.

The first daylight raid on Berlin was timed to take place as Göring was speaking to the Nation. The confusion and the bombs thudding down could be clearly heard. They even topped it up with an afternoon encore.*

Then the destruction of the Gestapo Headquarters in Oslo and the mass 2 Group attack on the Philips factory in Eindhoven, Holland. As an Airline Captain many years and thousands of hours later I had the pleasure of meeting one of my passengers who told me he had been there at the time and his most vivid recollection was of sitting in an office on the sixth floor and seeing a Mosquito flash past but below him!

It was quite common during those days to flash

* In Britain this raid was publicised as thumbing your nose at the school bully, because no one knew that the German Sixth Army at Stalingrad was on the point of surrender. The broadcast was on 31 January, 1943, the capitulation on 2 February. In the circumstances, six Mosquitos bombing Berlin in daylight must have made a difficult speech even more difficult. A recording (now in BBC archives) contains Göring's excuse for the Allied air raids: 'Have patience, the enemy cannot be paid back just yet; the German Air Force is busy against the Russians and cannot at the moment retaliate.' Nevertheless, Germany would win because of the Führer: 'God would not have raised him up like this only to see him fall.' And, pinching possibly from Oliver Cromwell, and excusing the introduction of National Socialist politics into the Army: 'Only those who know why they are fighting, fight well.' And what they were fighting against was, of course, Bolshevism and Plutocracy: 'a war of victory or annihilation'. Göring, at any rate, knew that the tide had turned.

over the enemy coast and see the German gun-crews lying out in the sun in bathing trunks. You could always bet that there would be a perfunctory burst of flak seconds later so that they could justify their existence.

Radio silence was the order of the day but one hapless crew captained by a pilot called Basil left their set on 'Transmit' the whole time. Their remarks were monitored at Marham, to where 105 and 139 had moved, and on their return they were greeted by a puce Groupie Kyle. 'Are you Basil?' he bellowed.

While we were at Horsham St Faith I met the WAAF Flight Sergeant who was to become my wife. On her birthday, 30 October, 1942, my flight commander, Bill Blessing, and myself set out to attack the Luftwaffe night-fighter aerodrome at Leeuwarden in Holland. This we did successfully, but I was hit by flak from the ground defences coming across the boundary of the airfield. The port engine was set on fire, the instrument panel and the windscreen disappeared with the nose of the aircraft. I was hit in the left leg–although I didn't even feel it at the time–and my observer, Les Hogan, in the arm.

At 40 feet or so control was tricky and I called to Les to press the extinguisher button on the port engine which I had feathered. He promptly pushed the Starboard one! The good engine was filled with foam, coughed once or twice and then, miraculously, the good old Merlin caught again and we snaked along almost sideways at about 160 mph. I had to jam my foot under the rudder-bar to keep it straight as the rudder-trim handle had been shot away. We went out over the aptly-named Frisian island of Overflakkee straight between two German ships who opened up on us. Luckily we were so low that they could not get their guns to bear down on us, and the ship on the port side hit the ship on the starboard side, starting a fire in the bows. I later claimed this as a 'possible' and got well and truly shot down by the Authorities.

During the return flight over the sea Les wound down the trailing aerial to try and signal base. The aerial hit the sea and Les yelled he had been hit again, but it was the handle whizzing round which had banged him in his seat.

We managed to get back to Marham but I couldn't go into cloud as we had no instruments and we were actually in the circuit when our long-suffering Merlin packed up; we went down into a nearby wood, skating along the tops of the trees, demolishing about thirty (according to the farmer who claimed compensation for them) before we came to a standstill and promptly blew up.

My feet had gone through the side of the fuselage and I was helpless, but Les Hogan stepped out of the front (there was no nose, it was in Leeuwarden), took my boot off, and we ran like mad despite the wound in my leg which was now making itself felt. We didn't have a scratch on us from the crash which had completely demolished the aircraft.

Had the Mosquito been a metal aircraft I am sure that my foot would have been severed, and I am sure that we were saved by the complete break-up of the aeroplane. After three weeks in Ely hospital we were back at Marham operating again.

I flew many aircraft after the Mosquito, over 50 types in fact, but remember it as the finest of its kind in the world and salute the designers, De Havilland, who never made a bad-looking aeroplane and who pressed on with its development despite a very lack-lustre Government.

Some of the finest aircrews who ever breathed

flew with 139 and 105 Squadrons from Horsham and Marham in those early days, and I am proud to have known them and flown with them.

The late W/Cdr John de Lacy Wooldridge, DSO, DFC and bar, DFM, who commanded 105 Squadron later on, wrote in his book *Low Attack* (Samson Low 1944):

For those of us who flew the Mosquitos on these attacks the memory of their versatility and their achievements will always remain. It would be impossible to forget such an experience as the thunderous din of twenty aircraft sweeping across the hangars as low as possible, setting course like bullets in tight formation for the enemy coast. The whole station would be out watching, and each leader would vie for the honour of bringing his formation lower across the aerodrome than anyone else. Nor would it be possible to forget the sensation of looking back over enemy territory and seeing your formation behind you, their racing shadows moving only a few feet below them across the earth's surface; or that feeling of sudden exhilaration when the target was definitely located and the whole pack were following you on to it with their bomb doors open while people below scattered in every direction and the long streams of flak came swinging up; or the sudden jerk of consternation of the German soldiers lounging on the coast, their moment of indecision, and then their mad scramble for the guns; or the memory of racing across The Hague at midday on a bright spring morning, while the Dutchmen below hurled their hats in the air and beat each other over the back. All these are unforgettable memories. Many of them will be recalled also by the peoples of Europe long after peace has been declared, for to them the Mosquito came to be an ambassador during their darkest hours.

Mosquitos flew by night as well as by day, at altitude as well as down on the deck, depending on the job they were doing; and in bad weather as well as good. Indeed, some marks, later in the war, when fully-equipped with effective navigation instruments, became virtually the first of the 'all-weather' fighters. For them, often the worst enemy was 'Sir Isaac Newton' (or just plain 'Isaac'), rather then Hermann Göring's aircraft and flak. Others lacked advanced instrumentation and, for them, Stationary searchlight beams pointing upwards beckoned the way.

A. Courtney, living in Gosport, Hampshire, joined 393 RE Searchlight Regiment of the Territorial Army in about 1936:

As searchlights were being used as 'Homing Beacons' for lost or damaged aircraft, we were involved constantly in performing this task. My unit selected me to visit an aerodrome for the purpose of liaison with the pilots. Our aim was to find out if the method used was satisfactory and, if necessary, make changes in our techniques which the pilots considered helpful. I spent approximately four days on an aerodrome. I cannot now remember its name, nor the date, but it was an enjoyable experience made more so by the fact that the squadron concerned flew Mosquitos, my favourite aircraft. A short time before I arrived this squadron had bombed a house in The Hague which it is alleged contained a mass of secret documents; I can clearly remember the story that the newspapers carried; one headed their article—'Mosquitos put bombs in front door of secret documents house in The Hague.'
On about the third day of my visit to the 'drome,

a pilot asked me if I would like a flip in a Mosquito. I just leaped at the opportunity. He said it was a training run. I sorted out a harness and parachute that fitted me from a row of six hanging on a rail in the open.

Three of us took off; the leader carried a navigator and we just followed in formation. It was a beautiful, warm, sunny day and we were flying at a height of about six to eight thousand feet, when, over the Salisbury Plain area, out of the sun at about two o'clock three American Thunderbolt fighters streaked down straight at us.

My pilot slammed the stick over to the left and we made a very powerful 90° bank to the left, shearing away from the Thunderbolts. This turned what could have been a disaster into a near miss. 'That was a close one, ' the pilot exclaimed as we levelled off back in formation.

After that we had a very enjoyable flight, returning after about an hour. When we went in to land, my pilot hit the ground a little hard and we bounced into the air. 'Sorry about that,' he said, giving the stick a little nudge forward. Ultimately he made a beautiful three-point landing. It was a flight I will never forget. I got the utmost pleasure listening to those two beautiful Rolls Royce engines purring away. The Mosquito was the most beautiful propellor-driven aircraft that has ever been designed, and De Havilland did a marvellous job with this one.

A tragedy occurred above me one night. I think it was in the Bracklesham, Birdham area of Sussex. A Mosquito and a Wellington collided above us. I can clearly remember all the wood of the Mosquito that fell around us. The rear turret of the Wellington landed in the mud of the harbour about 150 yards away.

The daylight low-level attack Mr Courtney read about must have been one of a series mounted towards the end of the war in Europe against Gestapo targets, including Amiens prison on 18 February, 1944; the HQ in The Hague on 11 April, 1944; and similar Gestapo buildings in Aarhus on 31 October, 1944; in Copenhagen ('Shell House') on 21 March, 1945; and at Odense on 17 April, 1945. These were undoubtedly evil institutions, and they were methodically picked off by the hedge-hopping Mosquitos as if by a sniper. Only in Copenhagen did a tragic accident occur.

One of the low-flying leading Mosquitos came too low, struck a flagpole and crashed into a convent school; some of the following Mosquitos, streaking across the city at high speed, took the great column of smoke, fire and dust for the presumably stricken target, and bombed the broken convent instead of Shell House. Many children were killed or maimed. The Danes forgave, because it was an error of war; not a deliberate slaughter.

Bad luck played a part, too, in an earlier raid when, on 25 September, 1942 four Mosquitos of 105 Squadron, led by S/Ldr Parry, were sent to Oslo to destroy the Gestapo HQ in Victoria Terrasse and the Army HQ in the KNA-hotellet. Svein Tonning, then a schoolboy, vividly recalls looking out of a third-storey window in the Norwegian capital and seeing three Focke-Wulf 190s flash past just above rooftop height. Four of these new, high-performance fighters of 3 staffel JG 5 had landed at Olso only that morning, and three were scrambled to meet the attack, chasing the Mosquitos up the fjord and over the city, picking off the last two. F/Sgt Carter's Mosquito crashed on fire into Lake Engervannet near Sandvika, but the other got back on one engine.

CHAPTER SIX
Night and Day Fighter (1942-1944)

Someone yells: 'A flare–look!'

There is a red light over Emsworth, wavering slightly. A trail of white smoke, tinged with black, shoots out behind it. The light grows larger and the smoke trail longer.

I murmur: 'It's like a comet. It's beautiful.'

The flare is suddenly whisked into motion . . . and we gaze, dumbfounded, wondering vaguely if it is some horrible new weapon.

There is a shout of: 'It's a plane!'

The red light is now a raging furnace, trailing white smoke and shedding black objects, and moving fast.

The blazing holocaust in mid-air dives abruptly, and breaks up. Particles of red flame float down by themselves. The main mass of fire curves earthwards at great speed, gradually going into a vertical plunge.

The horizon is quite light for some time after it has hit the ground.

From author's diary, 4 May, 1941, describing an air raid incident east of Portsmouth

The Battle of Britain and the 'Blitz' by night lasted from July 1940 to May 1941. In Britain it is rightly remembered as the Spitfire era. But after that, the bulk of the Luftwaffe–more than 2,000 first-line aircraft–was to be concentrated against Russia, leaving only small fighter and bomber forces in the West.

By the time the fighter versions of the Mosquito came into service, in April 1942–at the start of the 'Baedeker' Raids–the small attacks which, from time to time, were mounted by the Luftwaffe were of no importance. Indeed, they evoked protests from German planners because they took away bombing and minelaying aircraft from the British ports and seaways which, added to the U-Boat campaign, was a really serious threat, in favour of pure 'revenge' raids for the RAF's burning of Lübeck.

In 1940, British air defence by night was fairly ineffective. By 1942, when the first Mosquito night-fighters entered service, there had been considerable improvements; but immediate results could not be spectacular, because there was not much 'trade' about. Long term, it was to be a different matter.

At the time, these developments were highly secret; and even suspect to authority itself. Ignoring the sup-posed diet of carrots on which night-fighter 'aces' were supposed to be fed (a deliberate piece of 'disinformation' aimed at the enemy and wholly swallowed by the British public), thankfully forgetting the weird and far-from-wonderful proposals actually contemplated by authority–such as airborne searchlights and even aerial minefields, and ignoring suggestions in the popular press by public-spirited patriots to mount anti-aircraft guns on barrage balloons, the one and only problem was how to guide the fighter into position behind the enemy bomber, flying the same course, flying at the same height, and flying at the same speed.

In retrospect, it seems odd that fighters were not allowed to free-hunt along the route of the incoming bombers and pick them off when they became silhouetted above the glow of the fires caused by the burning of some unfortunate city centre or dockland. In the winter of 1940–1941, that might have paid dividends. It would have become unprofitable later, when radar-directed intercep-tions were almost the sole solution. These were to be achieved by a complex system of radars, ground control-lers, and 'black boxes' in the aircraft.

One of those who came into the system at an interesting early point was Bud Green from Vernon, British Columbia, who joined 410 Squadron, Royal

Canadian Air force, when he was around 21, about average for aircrew, and indeed ground crews also. When he left the Service it was as a Wing Commander with the AFC, 1,000 hours on twenty different marks of Mosquito, four years as a test pilot at RAE and a spell as Chief Flying Instructor at the RAF College, Cranwell.

In his view, radar had been in its infancy in 1936; by 1938 you could call it experimental; but in 1942, when his night-fighting career began, the boffins had miniaturised it so that radar sets could be fitted into aircraft.

It was surprisingly without fault. In spite of being operated by inexperienced radar mechanics and aircrew kids like us, there was only a small amount of malfunction. We didn't know how it worked or its origins (well, I didn't). Probably there were not enough expert people around at the time to explain. There was what was called the Chain Home Low–a link of radars at low level. What was known as GCI covered the area above that. On our miniaturised sets the 'blip' which was another aircraft was hard to see among the wiggly lines called the 'ground returns'–the radio waves reflected back by the earth. Night-fighting was a shared success. You couldn't succeed by yourself. The navigator, the radar operator, was the key to that success, peering into the tube and interpreting what he saw, saying, 'Go right, go left, go up, go down.' Having a companion close beside you also makes you brave–of that I'm sure.

The first type of airborne radar Bud worked with was the Mark IV on the Blenheim in 1942; followed by radars in the Beaufighter II and the Mosquito NF II.

An early Mark was surprisingly good, 80 per cent effective, I thought. The scanner was in the nose, an all-round scanner giving roughly four miles coverage ahead, and two miles coverage astern, so you couldn't be intercepted by anyone coming up behind you. At six miles range ahead, you only got a vague picture. The navigator, looking through his eye-piece into the tube, was watching two indicators–one for elevation (the height of the 'blip'), one for azimuth (where the 'blip' was on the horizontal plane). The set didn't work much below 5,000 feet because of the ground returns; really low down, all you got was 'mush'.

A later set, I think it was the Mark V, was the worst of the lot. There was a display on this set just for the pilot, and as I couldn't fly on instruments as well as watch a radar, I had it blanked out.

The Mark VIII was better. It was a series of concentric circles, but with a forward scanner only (no coverage behind you), but with enormously increased range–at least double.

We also had one Flight with a radio receiver–which would pick up German night-fighter transmissions.

Starting on Blenheims, Bud Green went on to Beau-fighters and then converted to the Mosquito.

On both the Beau and the Mossie there was a marvellous view forward; but you had whacking great engines beside you, so all night-fighters had to have shrouded exhausts. Without them, you couldn't see at all at night.

The beaufighter was heavy, solid, not fun at all to fly. Rather like flying the Forth Bridge in a thick fog. The Beaufighter throttle quadrant was large, so you had to make large movements to open the throttles; but the Mosquito throttle quadrant was short. The effect was startling. An astonishing increase in power; faster, lighter. A bit touchy before you got used to the throttles, but then you could play them like organ stops. This was my initial impression of the Mosquito. My second impression was how responsive to aileron movements.

I had two loves–the Tiger Moth and the Mosquito. The Mosquito was a superb design and a delight to fly. Like a lady, beautiful to look at, capricious, but if handled properly was a delight; had vices, as all ladies have–stalling was one. But one can't disassociate the design concept from Rolls Royce–because the engines were the key. No engine failed me in 1,000 hours. They were super engines.

Pressed to elaborate on the vices, particularly the chances of escaping from the aircraft, Bud Green summed up:

It was almost impossible to get out of a Mosquito in a hurry unless you had plenty of height. The conventional way out was through the starboard door in the floor; with height, the navigator could probably escape. Not so the pilot. The Mossie was not very stable, so as soon as you let go the stick . . . apart from that, the pilot would have to negotiate the obstacles wearing a seat-type parachute. The navigator's chute was better for restricted spaces. The cockpits were tiny.

The other way out was to jettison the hood; but the Mossie had a very high tail fin. I can only give a subjective answer, but I'd have preferred to go out over the top. In static tests on the ground, it was found possible to evacuate a Mossie in 30 seconds. But I'd say that in the air, at under 5,000 feet, your chances were nil.

With very little 'trade' at home, Bud was sent out on

a number of 'Intruder' or 'Ranger' patrols. The difference between the two seems slight, except that the targets on an Intruder mission were more specific than on a Ranger. They usually boiled down to airfields (interfering with German night-flying) and trains, trucks or barges (communications targets). On 17 May, 1943 Bud did a 'Ranger' to northern France.

We were given a reasonable entry point. The Seine in moonlight is easy to pick up. We were going up the Seine towards Paris at about 500 feet when either a Hudson or a Havoc came underneath on an exactly reciprocal course to ours; it was about 100 feet below us and was past in a flash, silhouetted against the river. This was my only near-miss (which I knew about). He probably never saw us.

Shortly afterwards, on this same trip, we were between Amiens and the coast, quite low. A searchlight briefly caught us. We were blinded and lost our horizon. It was quite frightening. Then the light AA opened up–with coloured tracer. Certainly red and white, and possibly other colours, too. My navigator said:

'Isn't that pretty!'

It was the first time I'd been shot at with tracer. You see it coming towards you, so slowly, then it goes past in different directions faster than the speed of sound–an extraordinary experience.

During this time we got clobbered underneath the starboard engine by something pretty hefty–20mm or 50mm? I heard a distinct thump, either a hefty shell or the tyre blowing, or both together, and saw holes in the starboard wing.

Coming back to land at West Malling we got two greens on the approach, touched down or PSP or a grid; and part of the undercarriage collapsed because the tyre was gone. The impact broke the

Mosquíto in half, and we skidded along in the front bit, hitting our heads violently on the canopy (no bone-domes then). The aircraft, with 150 bullet holes in it, was put on the scrap heap; and our nurses were cautious and wouldn't let us have a beer.

From an aircraft unwanted by both Air Ministry and Bomber Command, the Mosquito was now being given all sorts of tasks made possible by its speed and range. In May 1943, Bud Green was sent on detachment with other members of the squadron to Predannack in Cornwall as day fighter escorts to Halifax bombers towing Horsa gliders en route to the Middle East theatre of war, for use in impending airborne operations. These day-fighter escort duties were known as 'Insteps', and Bud flew four of them–21 and 28 May, 4 and 7 July 1943, in beautiful weather. In each case, the escort consisted of four Mosquitos.

We picked up the Halifaxes and gliders after they had taken off from Portreath, also in Cornwall. We were to escort them outside the normal range of UK-based fighter cover, past northern France, Spain and Portugal. We were worried about Ju 188s and the very long-range Focke-Wulf Condors. We could expect Focke-Wulf 190 fighters up to 100 miles out from the coast of France, so we gave it a wide berth. Then past northern Spain; and for Portugal, a neutral, we came closer, perhaps three miles.

The Halifax tugs and their glider tows flew at perhaps 125 mph. The Mosquito over-heated its engines at that speed, needing at least 180 mph. So instead of flying straight and level escort, we flew a scissors manoeuvre.

We saw nothing but sea and were up a long time– five-and-a-half to six hours. And the Mosquito was cramped. The glider pilots were very brave, with no engines and sitting there with nothing but sea under their seats.

We took about three hours going out, but it was faster back and also we took a more direct course, as we were not so much at risk as the Halifaxes and Horsas; we passed much nearer to Brest, but fast. On the way back, we might attack ships, but that was incidental; protecting the gliders and their tugs was the main thing.

On 13 October, 1943 Bud scored his first victory–he shot himself down. During an air-firing test at ground targets, a shell bounced back off the grass and hit one of his own engines, resulting in a single-engine landing. On 5 November, 1943 (Guy Fawkes Night) there was a different combat with a different ending.

He flew Mosquitos mainly from three aerodromes north of London–Acklington in Northumberland, Coleby Grange in Lincolnshire, and Castle Camps in Cambridgeshire–and usually covered the area Humber, Lincoln, Great Yarmouth. This was a bomber route to the industrial cities of the Midlands and the North. It did not offer so many targets as 'Bomb Alley'–the short route for fast bombers from Dover to London.

Most of the work of night-fighter crews during my time on ops–early 1942 to early 1944–was very, very dull. There was hardly any German activity at all. Night after night–and sometimes twice a night–we went up and intercepted only our own aircraft. *But* we did this in all weathers. We flew when no one else flew. They were not arduous trips, though. Relatively short, because we had to balance fuel reserves when on a patrol, to allow for possible combat. And, of course, we did day work as well.

On this night–5 November, 1943–I was flying a

patrol line in the middle of the Channel, with other Mosquitos flying on my right and on my left. Ground control could only handle a limited number of aircraft; it was sited at Wartling near Dungeness. I was instructed: 'Bandits on a southerly heading, height unknown–considerable numbers.'

We were taken over by a Controller who steered me towards them, then round them (at about 18,000–20,000 feet), until we picked them up on our own radar. A classic interception.

Once the navigator had picked up an aircraft on his AI, the ideal was for the pilot to come in below at a closing speed as slow as possible, but fast enough for evasive action if fired on. You had to match the speed before you got a visual contact, then open up the throttles to close in by eye. I came in too low–far too low–overtaking speed not high enough. I had to pull up at full throttle, but was still too slow.

Pointing upwards at 200 yards, I fired all four cannon and the four machine-guns. We were so close, I didn't need tracer or to allow for deflection. He never knew what hit him. It was totally devastating. He just blew up. I saw the crosses on it; thought it was an Me 410, but in fact it was a 217. I have the impression that a two-second burst from a Mosquito fighter would destroy a house.

My CO thought it was great, but I felt no elation. I was so tired, I couldn't have cared less. The work was so concentrated–the GCI instructions to listen to, the Nav's instructions to listen to.

By the end of 1943, significant changes had taken place. RAF Fighter Command became 'Air Defence of Great Britain'–in order to distinguish its functions from those of the fighter force assigned to the forthcoming invasion of Europe through Normandy, many of whose squadrons would soon be stationed in France and, later, the Low Countries, when these had been captured. Numerous headquarters concerned with planning for the long-awaited 'Second Front' were formed in London, and as I was posted to one of these late in the year, I witnessed the last fling of the Luftwaffe over London in what was called the 'Baby Blitz'. They came up 'Bomb Alley' in a bewildering mix of fast and slow aircraft and at varying heights. The slower types included the Dornier 217, the Junkers 88 and 188, and the 'Scalded Cats', the extremely fast Focke-Wulf 190 single-seater and the German version of the Mosquito, the twin-engined Messerschmitt 410. The latter two were very hard to catch, even for a Mosquito, because the speed differences were small and the time for interception so short. The Mosquito night-fighter was now up against, not enemy bombers, but enemy fighters. Had Air Ministry and Bomber Command succeeded in giving them gun-turrets, there would have been no interceptions whatever.

Whereas the early German night raids during the 'Blitz' period had been leisurely, long-drawn-out affairs–one bomber coming in each three minutes or so–because of the improved defences, the new German tactics were to come in fast and high, bomb flares drifting down with incendiaries mainly; and then, to take care of the fire-guards busily putting out the fire-bombs (which of course also served as target markers), the second wave would drop showers of small anti-personnel bombs which made only tiny craters. Nevertheless, one blew me 20 feet through the air, and I can certify that they did hit a 'Second Front' headquarters! But the weight of attack was negligible. The period January-April 1944 was historically interesting because it marked the last use of the manned bomber over London. The next German aircraft to arrive over the centre of the capital–on 15 June–was flying fast and low, held in searchlight beams and apparently on fire, trailing a bright white-red light before it dived to earth about a quarter-of-a-mile away from me.

I felt sorry for the crew, but need not have bothered– it was a V-1, a jet-propelled robot now dubbed a cruise-missile.

In fact, the first salvo often V-1s had been launched from Pas de Calais on 13 June, four of them reaching southern England. I saw the gunfire which marked the approach of one to Bethnal Green, but at that distance from central London it seemed no more than a reception for a casual raider from the impressive barrage of shells and rockets.

A new era in air attack had begun and a new method of defence would have to be devised.

CHAPTER SEVEN
Malta
(1943)

Notify all units, especially AA, that parachutists 82d Airborne will drop about 23.30 tonight July 11–12 on Farello landing field.
Pencilled message from US General Ridgway

John Keeling left his studies at the University of Oxford to join the RAF. By January 1943 he was with an operational squadron, No. 605, flying Boston IIIs at Ford on the Sussex coast.

> My training had been on Havocs but I did not do ops on the Boston because, soon after I arrived, they got delivery of Mosquitos and so, although I was a 'new boy', I got a Mosquito. I spent all February converting, and did my first op on 12 March to Caen; next night to Rennes. Both uneventful, low cloud, but we knew we had found the right place in both cases by the flak. Both were night intruder operations at low level; aerodromes were the primary targets, but if that was no go, then trains. We were armed with four cannon and four m.gs; there was a long-range fuel tank in the bomb-bay, so we carried two 250s under the wings.

On 6 June, 1943, John Keeling was posted to 23 Squadron, a night intruder squadron which had flown out to Malta in December 1942. At that time, Malta was probably the worst-bombed place on earth; it was home to the torpedo-bomber squadrons which harassed the

Axis Supply routes to North Africa. The purpose of night intruding was to patrol the vicinity of enemy aerodromes, particularly those handling night-fighters, and so harass them that they had no leisure to interfere with the torpedo-bombers or indeed any other Allied operations. Now, however, the face of the war had changed. The Axis forces in North Africa had surrendered, and the Allies were about to start a series of amphibious offensives which were to culminate on 6 June the following year in the invasion of Normandy and the conquest of half Europe. The first 'D-Day' was to be in July 1943, on the beaches of Sicily.

In June I flew a Mosquito VI from Lyneham to Portreath in Cornwall; then round Spain to Gibraltar, over the sea all the way. There was a short runway at Gibraltar, so we could not take off with enough fuel to make Malta direct. Instead I flew to Ras el Mar airport at Fez in Morocco. It was near Casablanca, and as I'd just seen the Humphrey Bogart film of that name, I wanted to see the place. So I put Casablanca on my route. It made a great contrast in weather. In Cornwall the days had been rainy; but in North Africa it was terribly hot, especially as I had the wrong clothes on. Then it started to rain and I stripped off and stood out in it– but the rainwater was hot, too! From Casablanca I went to Maison Blanche airport in Algiers, and then on to Luqa, the only airfield on Malta with runways long enough for Mosquitos.

The people were starving. There was a black market–with eggs at 2/6 each. There was no nightlife for us, we were worked hard at night, out over Sicily or Italy. I think about half of us were killed during the time I was there, although I can't check that. The most spectacular sight was the box barrage. The Ju 88s came in from the north-west, dived down on

Grand Harbour, Valetta, into an incredible fire-work display. They were very brave. Many were shot down, because there was AA all round Grand Harbour, including the low level AA against dive-bombing.

On 14 June John Keeling flew the first of 33 operations from Malta over Eastern Sicily, where Montgomery's Eighth Army from Africa was shortly to land; and the following night another one over Western Sicily, the imminent target of General Patton's US Seventh Army sailing from the ports of Oran, Algiers and Bizerta. For the next four nights he went to Italy, touring up the mountainous western coast bordered by the Tyrrhenian Sea, shooting up trains.

Because of the mountainous terrain they were in tunnels half the time, instead of in the open–and one didn't want to follow a train into a tunnel. They had overhead cables for power, so no sizeable flak could be mounted on the trains. There is a limit to what one can see, even in moonlight, apart from the electrical sparks from the overhead connection, so we fired at the front of the trains with our guns and put our two 250 lb bombs on the track. We also patrolled aerodromes but the Italians got scared and stopped flying at night. So we'd done our job. We were ordered to stop the enemy flying, and we did. Then we set out to create trouble, like small boys breaking windows. In the Mosquito, we had the fastest manoeuvrable aircraft in southern Europe; only the FW 190 was faster, and they were in northern Europe. It was not like flying a heavy bomber. We felt like the small boy given a catapult and sent down the High Street to see how many windows he could break. I took on only what were apparently military targets. We were told that all

95

trains moving at night were military trains; no civilians were moving at night.

From Malta we could patrol mid-Sicily, Battapaglia, Salerno, Naples, German airfields on the Catania plain, near Mount Etna, and also airfields at Taranto and Foggia. We could get as far as the coast of Albania and patrol there. But the invasion of Sicily was pending, so the airfields on the Catania plain and the plain of Foggia were more usual.

It was exciting, a turning point of the war. We were invading Europe, with the Americans there in force; we were winning. It was success–and we were in the forefront of the attack.

The day before the invasion of Sicily, there were 24 squadrons on Malta, so it was a bit crowded, with lots of Dakotas at Luqa. I went up to do a test–ten minutes in daylight–but it was an hour and a quarter before I could get a spot to land on. Priority was being given to Spitfires coming back low on petrol.

There were also nightfighter Mosquitos based on Malta for the protection of the island itself–which, when John Keeling got there, was being bombed nightly. But when he took off on the night of 9 July, his squadron's job was to protect the invasion fleets. The British force was passing to the eastward of Malta, bound for the beaches of eastern Sicily, while the American ships, having first steered the usual course for Malta-bound convoys coming from the west, turned due north and, passing to the west of Malta, headed for the middle of the southern coastline of Sicily. The arrival of the American troops was to be preceded by a drop of four battalions–2,700 paratroopers–of the US 82nd Airborne Division onto the high ground overlooking those beaches in the Gulf of Gela; but the troop-carrying Dakotas, from a mixture of high winds and too-complicated plans, spewed their contents along a 60-mile stretch of southern Sicily. What happened in the

British sector was worse. American Dakotas were to fly in 1,600 men of the British 1st Airborne Division in 133 troop-carrying gliders. Twelve of those gliders reached their objective, a bridge near Syracuse. But most of the airborne men were unceremoniously dumped into the sea in full kit, together with their brigadier.

The story went round the whole British Army at lightning speed, that the pilots of the transports had never been under fire before, and as the formidable flak came up at them, simply unlinked their tow-lines, let the gliders go down anywhere, and roared off out of it. John Keeling confirmed that the Dak pilots had never seen flak before and, from his own very personal experience, that both Augusta and Syracuse were well defended. But he added that the British landings were on the east coast of Sicily, with a strong west wind blowing offshore on invasion night, which was a contributory reason for the Daks dropping people to the east, over the sea. 'Nevertheless, the Dak pilots were pretty unpopular after that.'

This chaotic use of expensive airborne troops caused a second drop to be delayed 24 hours. In June, General Eisenhower had approved a plan to drop the two remaining regiments of the 82nd Airborne Division as immediate reinforcements, to be withdrawn once the beach-head was secured. General Ridgway was apprehensive about flying in this force over the guns of the Navy. The British Navy had a hard-earned reputation for shooting at anything that flew (and indeed, up to now what had flown over them was mainly hostile); and the American Navy was to be not one whit behind them. Ridgway demanded a safe-conduct over the invasion fleet massed in the Gulf of Gela for his 144 Dakotas bound for Farello airfield west of Gela. At first, the Navy refused it, then said they could enforce a ban on firing, but what about the many merchant ships also anchored offshore? These too were armed (and indeed there were many AA guns already ashore to guard the beach-head against air attack. Ridgway went to General Patton, commanding the US Seventh Army, and Patton's staff 'coaxed' an agreement from the Navy that AA fire would be withheld over the routes the planes were due to fly. Messages were sent out to both sea and land units notifying them of the routes and that the Dakotas would come in low at 700 feet over the invasion beaches.

After darkness had fallen on 11 July, some German aircraft took off to bomb the American beach-head. From Tunisia, 144 Dakotas were airborne with 2,000 American paratroopers aboard and began to drone out over the Mediterranean for southern Sicily. From Luqa airfield in Malta, John Keeling's Mosquito took off for an intruder sortie to northern Sicily.

I had been told that a flak-free passage over the invasion fleet lying off the coast, had been arranged. I flew in from the south at 150 feet.

We had no radar, only a DF aerial on the roof to tell us the way home.

The Germans arrived first, or at least some of them did; that much seems certain. The American General Bradley was a witness to what followed. Soon after dark the usual nightly raid began, with the thump of guns, the roar of aero engines, the whistling and crump of bombs. Then it stopped, and the moon shone down on a calm, Mediterranean Sea. The first wave of the 144 Dakotas droned up from the south at 700 feet and turned away towards their drop zone.

Then a single gun fired.

Instantly, hundreds of guns joined in. The vulnerable troop carriers twisted and turned like scared birds, ready-lights blinking in the cabins as the pilots tried to get rid of their load of armed men. Some of those who jumped, mistaken for Germans, were shot as they neared the ground.

Afterwards, the AA gunners, land and sea, maintained

that more German aircraft had come in on the tail of the first Dakotas. Maybe. Or perhaps it was just John Keeling, flying in at 150 feet, well below the level of the transport aircraft, assured that he had a flak-free passage.

We were coming in low from the south to the bight where the ships lay. WHISH! A mass of ships, and they all opened up on me!

There was a resounding bang, and the gauge on my long-range fuel tank went to nought in seconds. I fired Verey signals, but they took no notice. Now, I hadn't enough fuel to carry on to northern Sicily, so I went back. We found that a cannon shell had exploded inside the fuel tank which, fortunately, was full to the brim.

Of course, if the tank had been part-empty, there would have been fumes which would have ignited and John Keeling's Mosquito would have joined the 23 Dakotas lost that night, along with 20 per cent of the paratroop force. Sixty or so shot-damaged Daks struggled back to Tunisia. The dawn of 12 July revealed the broken bodies of many aircraft lying in the surf. Had the drowned soldiers been enemy, it might have ranked as a famous victory. As it was, the airborne generals forever after tried to avoid over-flying 'friendly' ships.

Next day, 13 July, John Keeling was directed to cover the 'heel' of Italy, flying to Taranto and Lecce, and seeing the fires caused already by other Allied aircraft. Then on 15 July to Naples, followed on 17 July by the long haul to Rome itself, although they could not stay there long. Their Mosquito's endurance was four-and-a-half hours plus half-an-hour margin. On 19 July to Salerno and south of Battapaglia, bombing railways and roads and snooping generally. On 23 July Foggia, into light and heavy flak; on 27 July, dawn over the Lipari Islands.

Then on into August. On the 14th the Bay of Taranto, where they bombed a railway junction and landing craft.

We were always told before an op that there would be a submarine waiting offshore on a particular date at a particular time–if we were shot down but escaped capture. It would be there just the one night, midnight to 1 a.m. We were to flash a torch from the shore. Was this true? Or was it to keep us happy? We were also told what the German Verey light code was (it changed every eight hours).

On the night of 15–16 August we were 50 miles north of Naples when we had a big end go in one engine. The Germans still held a bit of Sicily near Messina, while we held the Catania plain. We now had to come back on one engine. When I tried to climb high enough to get over the Sicilian mountains, our one good engine started over-heating; and I couldn't go through the Messina route because of flak. So I headed south to western Sicily, calling *May Day* as we passed over Palermo.

I got a reply and was told there was a landing strip on the beach. I asked them to put out two vehicles with headlights pointing downwind. I saw those lights, landed, and came to a halt by the second vehicle. The people were Americans, who gave us a tent to sleep in. When we got up next morning we could see Palermo to the west–and the barrage balloons flying over it. 'Thank God they weren't there last night!' I said. 'They were!' replied a Yank.

On 17 September there was another notable entry in the logbook. Rome again-they bombed Ciampino airport, well known to the modern package tourist, with two 250-pounders placed on the hangar apron from 200 feet amid heavy flak. By now, everything was topsy-turvy in Italy, the Italians wanting to surrender and the Germans most unwilling to let them. The diplomatic situation was still obscure, when John Keeling took off on 22 September, 1943, for Lecce on the 'heel' of Italy:

> Our Intelligence Officer said that one of our Flight Commanders, missing for a few days, was reported to be at Lecce. Allied troops had landed on both sides of the 'heel' north of Lecce, and so I flew off, expecting the airfield to be in Allied hands. But I was greeted, after landing, by several dozen Italian soldiers with rifles. There was nothing I could do about that, so I got out. An Italian officer came up. I asked him:
>
> 'Am I under arrest?'
>
> He replied: 'No! No! Haven't you heard?–we changed sides yesterday!'
>
> The Germans had retreated north, it seemed, so they took me to the Italian Officers' mess and gave me so much to drink that I was incapable of flying back that night. They toasted us:
>
> 'Our friends! We are allies now!'
>
> That night I slept in silk pyjamas between clean linen sheets–something I hadn't seen for years!

Under Marshal Kesselring, the Germans made a most remarkable recovery in Italy. The last of John Keeling's 33 ops from Malta on 15 October, 1943, might have been an omen. It was an attack carried out from 100–200 feet on transport heading south from Rome. Reinforcements for the Gothic line. The Allies were hoping for Vienna before the bitter Italian winter, but Hitler had informed Kesselring: 'The Führer has decided to defend the Apennine front and to hold upper Italy, not only until late autumn, but indefinitely.' And winter came.

After his tour on Mosquitos, John Keeling went to Debert in Nova Scotia, as an instructor on the type. On 21 August, 1944 the pupil had the aircraft on the approach and was dangerously close to stalling speed, for the Mosquito landed at anything between 120–150 mph, depending on type and weight. Most approached at 150, crossed the hedge at 135, and touched down at 120 (although the Mark 30 night-fighters with full load approached at 180 and crossed the hedge at 155). If it was allowed to stall, a Mosquito simply fell out of the sky. On this approach, Keeling warned his pupil: 'You're too slow.' But instead of giving throttle to keep speed up, the pupil put the nose down to gain speed–and went straight into the ground. The Mosquito broke its back, the wreckage rapidly surrounded by a pool of leaking petrol. 'I had to get out the top way, and another instructor said that I was 30 yards clear of the plane before it had stopped moving!'

Keeling declined a posting to Burma; and instead went to Pershore, near Cirencester, for ferry duties, mainly to the Middle East; sometimes flying a Mosquito as leader to Spitfires, showing them the way.

Once, with six experienced Spitfire pilots, I took off with three Spits on each side. All the Spits were airborne and had their wheels up before my Mosquito had left the ground!

Another time, at Biskra in the northern Sahara, I had to be towed out onto the runway for take-off, to avoid over-heating the engines.

I remember coming back to England after a ferry journey to Cairo, with bananas. One bunch was covered but the other bunch was showing. So there was I, walking up the platform at Waterloo Station, a parachute on my shoulder, and holding two bunches of bananas. As I passed a mother with her small daughter, the little girl said: 'Mummy, what are those?'

'Those are bananas,' she replied, so I asked: 'Would you like one?'

Then other children came up for bananas. I remember the mystification on the children's faces, delight on the mothers' faces.

Of course, in England no one had seen bananas (or oranges, or ice-cream) for years.

Peace came in August 1945, and in January the following year John Keeling returned to his studies at Oxford, taking an economics degree and becoming a chartered accountant.

CHAPTER EIGHT
Photo-Reconnaissance, Europe (1943-1944)

Various types of aircraft were used by the RAF for photography during the Second World War. These included the Lancaster, the Wellington, the Blenheim, the Hudson, the Hurricane, the Buffalo and the Hellcat. Two only were outstanding: the Spitfire (in various marks) and the Mosquito (in the PR I, II, IV, VIII, IX, XVI, 32 and 34 versions). Both were unarmed, relying on speed and height to evade the enemy. The 'phoney' war period in France during the winter of 1939–40 had disposed entirely of the accepted RAF idea that a light bomber with defensive armament was the most suitable transport for cameras; the Blenheims had been massacred both by flak and fighters, whereas the first experimental Spitfires had covered twice as large an area and without loss. The man who had proved this, F. S. Cotton, was an outsider who was sacked by RAF politicians as soon as he had developed the technique and built up a unit to do the work.

Good though the Spitfire was, on most counts the Mosquito was better. It had twice the range, more room to house a much superior camera installation, and a navigator to help the pilot fly precisely the right track. On the other hand, an enemy tended to take more offence at being overflown by a twin-engined aircraft which might be carrying bombs than by a single-seat fighter. At first, there was not much difference in speed; later, the Mosquito was faster than the Spitfire, faster than the Me 109.

For long-distance flights the camera set-up was one used extensively by both the Americans and the Germans: a single short-lensed instrument to take pictures covering a large area in one photograph; and two large long-focal-length cameras to take big, big pictures of small, small targets within the larger overall area. Oblique photographs facing forwards could be taken through the nose, and cameras mounted in both wings gave stereo. Some of the cameras had film magazines accessible in flight, so they could be changed.

The first PR Mosquito (which was also to be the first operational Mosquito) was delivered to the RAF on 2 June, 1941, and named Benedictine (they were all to bear the name of a drink). As previously, this aircraft's first 'op' was on 17 September, 1941, and her last on 4 December the same year, when she was shot down by flak over Bergen. This was the first loss of a PR Mosquito after 88 successful sorties. By March 1942, improvements made it possible for PR Mosquitos to cover northern Norway, East Prussia, and northern Italy. In that month, by shallow-diving, a Mosquito out-ran an Me 109. By April 1943, further developments had made the Mosquito the fastest aeroplane in the world above 20,000 feet.

The contest which developed between the intercepting fighters and the solitary spy-planes became a duel for height. The first photo-recce plane I ever saw–it was on 18 August, 1940, after Stuka attacks on local aerodromes–was so high that it was completely invisible; but it was pulling a mile-long white 'smoke' trail behind it in a ruler-straight line. It was probably a Junkers 86P with a pressurised cabin. What later became known as 'contrails' are set off by certain air masses and, particularly in winter, were found to occur as low as 23,000 feet Where the head of the growing white worm was, there

105

was the spy plane, position, course and height indelibly marked on the sky for all–including the defending fighters–to see. The interceptor could climb to be in the right position and at the right height for a diving, firing pass.

An ordinary photo-recce machine would automatically turn back and make for home, the moment the pilot discovered he was in the sign-writing business. With the Spitfire and the Mosquito it was otherwise. They simply climbed higher. In 1942 the normal altitude for a photo-recce machine was 22,000 feet. The records for photo-coverage of the Berlin area show a steady increase of height throughout 1943–by April the PR machines were approaching 30,000 feet and by December were at heights of between 33,000 feet and 36,000 feet. By February 1944, the RAF was forced to fly at heights of just below or just above 40,000 feet. That was the peak of Luftwaffe effectiveness. At that time the US F-5s could make only a little over 30,000 feet, a very dangerous altitude. As the Mosquitos flew at economical cruising speed, a German fighter could, when perfectly controlled from the ground, make virtually faultless interception–only to have the Mosquito pilot turn up his engine boost and 'walk away' from his pursuer.

It was a rare event, initially, for a German flyer to shoot down a high-altitude Mosquito; promotion sometimes rewarded the successful pilot. From 1942 to March 1943 Klemens Rausch was an NCO radio operator with the HQ of I Gruppe, Jagdgeschwader 1 at Mönchengladbach in the Rhineland. Sound locators were still in use and the radar system was not so sophisticated as it was to become later, because the homeland was not under serious attack; indeed, a Germany appeared to be winning the war.

I recall an occasion when a sound locator picked up a very high-flying machine of unknown type coming in from the direction of the Scheldt Estuary. The duty pilot that day was Fähnrich Bugai of 1 Staffel of JG 1. He was ordered to take off, climb and intercept the unknown aircraft on its return flight towards the Scheldt. Major Losigkeit controlled the interception; my job was to keep the plot. For the first time the Major had the use of the recently introduced Freya-type radar and he decided to track the intruder only, as it was flying a straight course, and give radio instructions to Bugai which should result in the Bf 109-F intercepting the intruder when Bugai had a height advantage, so that he could gain speed by diving. Shortly afterwards we learned that the machine was a Mosquito and that it had been shot down. According to what I heard from the pilots, the Mosquito could reach a speed of 600 kph and it could only be caught in this way.

After this success, Bugai was promoted to Leutnant, and flew to Berlin to receive congratulations officially; but on his return flight there was low cloud covering the hilltops and he flew into the slopes of the Teutoburger Wald and was killed.

The more normal effect of meeting a Mosquito was frustration, mixed with admiration. This was certainly the reaction of Klaus H. Krebs, who was flying a later type of Messerschmitt than Bugai's 109-F. He wrote to me in September 1987:

I can only give a brief report of an encounter with a Mosquito, which proved to be so impressive that I can still see it in my mind's eye even to this day, and in every detail.

It was July 1944, and we were hovering at roughly 11,000 metres above France, with a Gruppe of about 25 Bf 109-G6s (the high-altitude hunter version of the 109), when a single Mosquito was seen

107

flying at our altitude. My Gruppe commander Hauptmann Weissenberger (at that time with 205 victories to his name) turned towards it but had little success in catching up.

Shortly afterwards, it seemed that the Mosquito pilot had noticed our presence. We saw a 'black fart' suddenly come out of his exhausts . . . and he smoothly drew away from us, without the slightest hint of effort or agitation. It was pointless to even consider attacking this aeroplane with 25 Bf 109s.

For me, to this day the Mosquito has remained a miracle plane of its time.

It was not only the enemy who were impressed by the swift performance of lone Mosquitos. Robert R. Lopiano, while serving with the USAAF, also experienced it.

I was a tail gunner on a Flying Fortress (B-17F) on a mission to bomb Regensburg and fly on to Africa. Well, as luck would have it, we blew an engine at the French coast. After discussion between our pilot and turret gunner (the Flight Engineer) they decided we would never make it to Africa. We aborted the mission and turned back to England.

Our navigator got us over land, but was not sure of our location. At this time I noticed a twin-engine ship closing in as rapidly as a Spitfire. Never having seen such a plane, I called to the pilot that I had spotted an unidentified aircraft.

After a few shaky minutes and by contacting a ground station, they acknowledged us as a friendly crippled aircraft heading for home. We were escorted back to base by this great airplane with speed to burn. Since then I've always had a soft spot in me for the Mosquito.

While an aircraft of ordinary performance might get away with the occasional penetration of enemy territory, the Spitfire and the Mosquito made routine, regular penetrations deep into Europe for five years of war, and lost few aircraft while doing it. The information they brought back was often vital.

Of course the photographs, once taken, had to be interpreted; and what was most important was continuous coverage, so that changes at various sites could be spotted and guesses made as to what they represented. One key investigation began in April 1943, into what we now call the 'V' weapons. There was the development and testing ground at Peenemunde in the Baltic and then the appearance of weird concrete structures on the French coast, principally in Pas de Calais opposite Dover and London. On 23 June, 1943 Flight Sergeant E.P.H. Peek, flying a Mosquito, brought back exceptionally clear photographs of Peenemunde. These, when studied closely, showed four small tailless aircraft. Now knowing what to look for, the interpreter, Constance Babington-Smith, was able to make out similar shapes in a number of fuzzy photographs taken earlier. They proved to be an experimental liquid-rocket propelled Messerschmitt fighter, the Me 163. On those latest, clear pictures Babington-Smith for the first time recognised dark streaks on the airfield as being caused by jet engines. The signs of V-1, V-2, and V-3 still had to be recognised. But the time of the 'cruise' missile and the stratospheric rocket had come. Britain and Belgium were to be the targets.

Reconnaissance by night became important, particularly when Allied air superiority by day forced the enemy to make his major troop and supply movements at night; and enormously powerful photoflash flares were developed. These weighed 60 lbs and a PR Mosquito could carry six of them. Each one could provide 120,000,000 candle power.

Squadron Leader Bill Aston, DFC, of 544 PR Squadron,

sometimes flew Spitfires but more usually Mosquitos with Flight Lieutenant Pete Fielding as his observer. In November and December of 1943 they ranged widely over Europe, going to Annecy and the Franco-Italian frontier; to Zurich, Trento and Bolzano on other trips (landing back at Benson with only 20 gallons of fuel left). In January, they fired six flash bombs on Abbeville; and the same again on Cherbourg a few nights later; and then to the Biarritz area. When Bill Aston took off in his Mosquito on 29 January, 1944 he had logged 1,934 hours and 50 minutes, many of them at night and in bad weather, and it was his 175th operational sortie. Across the right-hand columns of his logbook are printed the words 'DID NOT RETURN'.

I think I hold the dubious distinction of falling out of a Mosquito from the highest altitude, quite by accident, I might say. I was flying a Mosquito Mark 9, LR-430, over France on 29 January, 1944 on a night photographic mission, when we self-destructed at 35,000 feet. The aircraft exploded in a microsecond and, fortunately, I was wearing my pilot-type parachute which I eventually managed to open just a split-second before hitting the ground. I had free-fallen from 35,000 feet to about 500 feet. Fortunately, it was dark and I was blind anyway from the explosion (of the photo-flash bombs), so had no idea that 'mother earth' was so close. Flt/Lt Pete Fielding was killed as he had no time to attach his observer-chute when the aircraft blew up.

While on the way down from 35,000 feet–and remember it was a dark night–when I regained consciousness, I was frantically searching for the 'D'-ring to open the parachute. Couldn't find it. I eventually found it up by my left shoulder. I had obviously twisted in the harness. As I located the release and operated it, I heard a bang as the

110

parachute deployed and I hit the ground at the same time.

It was January, and I guess there had been considerable rain and that I must have landed in the softest, muddiest field in France! My first thoughts were to escape. I got up and started to run, only to go flat on my face in the mud, as I still had the 'chute attached to me.

Since it was pitch dark, I didn't realise that I was blind. However, I managed to pick up the 'chute with the idea of hiding it to avoid subsequent detection. By now I couldn't walk–all my muscles had seized up. I crawled through the mud for about half-an-hour, still clutching the 'chute, and eventually found a ditch and hid the 'chute under a pile of dead leaves.

By now my teeth were chattering with the cold and the aftermath of the experience. I heard a dog barking in the distance and headed off towards it. After about an hour of slow and difficult crawling, I found a gravel path and started to holler in my broken French: 'I am an English aviator!' 'People came out, but of course I couldn't see them.

It was now about midnight. I was carried into what I gathered was a farmhouse and, through a mass of French, someone eventually spoke to me in English, told me that I was with the French Maquis, and asked me for my name, rank and number. After a while, I was told that London would be notified that I was alive.

Later, I was told that because of my injuries I would probably die without medical attention (little did they know how wrong they were!). I was a liability to this organisation, unable to move, and they said they had no alternative but to hand me over to the Germans. This they did.

I received no medical attention of any sort for the

next six months and was subjected to many beatings by the Gestapo in the process. I eventually finished up in Stalag Luft 3. It took me about six months to recover my sight.

Some one-and-a-half years later, on my return from the 'holiday' camp, I got straight into a Mosquito and flew it with no refresher training whatsoever. I continued to fly Mosquitos on and off up to the end of 1949, when I graduated from the Empire Test Pilot School. I now have well over 20,000 hours of pilot command time and am currently flying the Boeing 767.

A contemporary of Bill Aston, who also passed through the Empire Test Pilot School, was Wing Commander S. McCreith, AFC, MRAeS. In Malaya in 1955, as CO of a PR Squadron operating during the 'emergency', it fell to him to pick the crew who would carry out the last operation by an RAF Mosquito. But back in March 1944 (when Aston was being interrogated by the Gestapo), McCreith was at No 8 Operational Training Unit converting to the Mosquito for high-altitude strategic photographic reconnaissance. Among the machines there was one of the first prototypes. At Benson in Oxfordshire, prior to an overseas ferry flight, McCreith was introduced to a much later version designed for PRU work, the Mosquito Mark XVI.

The Mark XVI had a pressure cabin which maximised to a pressure differential of 2 lbs per square inch, which gave a useful reduction in the cabin altitude, particularly as this Mark with two-speed, two-stage super-chargers and paddle-blade propellers could cruise comfortably at 35,000 feet. They did have a snag in that some aircraft did not control the engine rpm too well, so that the revs surged slightly and the two engines were never synchronised properly. The range was extended with the bomb-bay tank and under wing drop-tanks as standard.

A pair of split F52/36-inch lens cameras were installed in the rear a fuselage, split from vertical to increase the lateral coverage, and controlled by a Type 35 control in the bomb-aimer's nose position so that the cameras would turn over at pre-set intervals. This ensured a 60 per cent overlap between succeeding exposures and therefore gave a stereo-pair of photographs. In the forward end of the bomb-bay was another camera with a six-inch lens which gave a series of small-scale photographs to assist the interpreters in plotting the large-scale 36-inch photographs. When in the target area the navigator went down into the bomb-aimer's a position in the nose to give the pilot the usual directions onto target and switched on the cameras accordingly.

Normal operating height over Europe was about 30,000 feet, which was a bit above effective height for the very efficient German 88-mm gun, this being the most common. The 105-mm gun was not widely deployed and tended to be only around the heavily-defended areas.

As with all Marks of the Mosquito, the PR versions had excellent performance and good handling characteristics, particularly valuable at high operating altitudes. It provided a stable and manoeuvrable camera platform and was a great success in this role from the outset.

In common with most aircraft of that era there was no hydraulic accumulator, with the result that services such as the retraction of the undercarriage went at a slow rate. This was a major snag. The aircraft had high single-engine safety speeds and it would have helped to get rid of the high-drag undercarriage quickly, not only on take-off but for a single-engine overshoot. This was a hazardous operation which had to be initiated very early on the approach with plenty of height in hand. Also the slow lowering of undercarriage and flaps on the approach for a single-engine landing had to be taken into account.

One other pity was that the aircraft was never fitted with handed propellors (rotating in opposite directions), as this would have eliminated the torque effect on take-off. It was necessary to lead with the port throttle and put the power on fairly slowly until the rudder became effective; with handed propellors the take-off would have been much quicker and shorter, and the single-engine safety speed would have been reached sooner. Only a little later the DH 103–the Hornet–came along with this refinement, and it was spectacular!

McCreith and his navigator, Don Pizzy, ferried a Mosquito out to North Africa and then joined 680 PR Squadron base HQ just outside Cairo. The Squadron had detached flights of Spitfires in Cyprus and Mosquitos at Tocra near Benghazi. On 30 August, 1944, the Mosquito flight moved from North Africa to San Severo, just north of Foggia in Italy (the target, the previous year, for John Keeling's Mosquito intruder from Malta). San Severo was now the base of the Allied Photographic Reconnaissance Wing, which included 60 South African Air Force Squadron with Mosquito PR XVIS and 681 PR Squadron with Spitfires. There was also a squadron of USAAF P-51 Mustang fighters.

The runway was of PSP (Pierced Steel Planking), so there was a hell of a racket on touch-down, but of course these airstrips could be laid down quickly once the land had been levelled. We lived in tents, as we had done in Egypt and North Africa, but it

114

was a bit more civilised to have them pitched in a vineyard. There were no hangars, so all the maintenance was carried out in the open air; as always, the ground crews did sterling work. Up to the time I was shot down (Friday, 13th October, 1944!) the conditions were quite reasonable: dry, if a bit dusty; with no particular weather problems for operations, apart from the obvious one, ever present, of cloud cover in the target areas which aborted photography. I believe that after I left they had a fairly hard winter in that part of Italy, which restricted flying a good deal.

This Allied PR Wing complemented a similar UK-based effort with photographic coverage of Eastern Europe out to the areas of Russian activity. Targets were many and varied: bomb-damage assessment as soon as possible after raids was about the top priority, followed by railway marshalling yards, ports and rivers for shipping movements, factories, roads for troop movements, and so on. Clear weather was essential both to locate the targets and to obtain good photographs; but at the same time it was not a good thing to leave great long contrails, either persistent or non-persistent, so there tended to be a certain amount of juggling with heights.

On Friday the 13th of October, 1944, we were on an Ops Immediate sortie to cover the River Danube from Vienna to Budapest, to see if any shipping had been sunk as a result of mining by Wellingtons. When we arrived over Vienna the Americans were busy bombing an oil refinery on the north-western outskirts of the city, so the defences were well and truly alerted. We had to come somewhat lower than usual to about 26,000 feet to fly below a layer of cirrus cloud and we were chased by 88-mm flak most of the way over defended areas.

We finished the job and turned for home, but

shortly after lost all the glycol from the starboard engine which I then feathered. It was no problem to go back to San Severo on one engine but we could not maintain height; so descended steadily.

Somewhere near Lake Balaton in Hungary, over open country, two rounds of 88-mm came up, one off the port and the other bang in front of the nose, an extremely near-miss. The result was a long black smear down the port mainplane, and I guessed what the trouble was before looking at the oil pressure gauge reading zero.

We should have bailed out, but I thought to press on and try to make Yugoslavia; so I kept the port engine running until it started to shake about as the bearings began to go; I then feathered the port and unfeathered the stone-cold starboard to coax a little more mileage.

We eventually crash-landed near Keszthely at the southern end of Lake Balaton, made a muck of it because, with only one engine wind-milling, the flaps did not go down; and we ploughed through a wood. We came out at the far side, on fire, and with Don and myself sitting up front with nothing around us, just like the Wright Brothers.

Don had a broken arm and I was knocked out, plenty of surface damage but nothing broken.

We were scooped up by Hungarian Army people and taken to a doctor for first aid, then to hospital in Keszthely. I was heavily concussed, so my memory of that time is very vague, but we eventually left the hospital under armed guard by train to Budapest where we were separated into solitary confinement in the civil prison on the outskirts of the city. This was used as a collection point for Allied aircrews who had been shot down.

While in the prison I had a good view, while standing on the bedhead, of a Russian air raid one

116

night when they buzzed at low level over the city, bombing by random distribution!

A bunch of us, all officers, were shipped out in a cattle truck across Europe, having been handed over to the Luftwaffe. I did not see my navigator, Don Pizzy, until after the war as he went off to a POW camp for NCOs. I suppose, strictly speaking, having been captured in Hungary by Hungarians, I should not have been handed over to the Germans, but one cannot argue.

After a long, slow journey we arrived at Dulag Luft, the Luftwaffe interrogation centre at Frankfurt -am-Main. I was interrogated by a Luftwaffe major who had been in the First World War, and I think he just wanted to talk since his questions to me were almost non-existent. For example, he told me that he had been a POW in Edinburgh and his guard taught him a bit of doggerel which went: 'We are both young and flighty, so why the pyjamas and why the nightie?' He leaned back in the chair and roared with laughter.

The only serious question he asked was about H2S, of which equipment I knew absolutely nothing. It was Bomber radar and I can only assume that they did not have full knowledge of its capabilities.

After a short time I was put on a train to Stalag Luft III at Sagan in Upper Silesia. So my interrogation was something of a non-event. Mind you, quite a long time had elapsed since I was shot down, so I guess there was very little interest in me anyway. One thing the major did say was:

'Why do you go on taking pictures of the Danube? We could let you have plenty of picture postcards.'

So they obviously had a complete report on the fact that the aircraft was a PR Mosquito and the details of my flight path.

After the war I went back to Benson, this time on

117

the Photographic Reconnaissance Development Unit where I acquired a taste for research and development work which coloured my subsequent career.

The 'interrogation' might not have been so carelessly superficial as it appeared, for the technique used was exactly that employed by the Imperial German Air Force in the Great War. This has been described in detail by a practised interrogator, Hans Schröder, in his book *An Airman Remembers,* published in English translation just before the Second World War. The prisoner is treated kindly and the impression given that the Germans are not really interested in him because they know everything already. The name of his CO, for instance (obtained from a previous prisoner), the fact that there is a decent bar in St Pol–and a devilish nice girl, little Mary. Surely the existence of little Mary cannot possibly be a military secret, some previous prisoner must have thought. And he was wrong, for a casual mention to the next man, as a kind of joke, would impress on him that his interrogator knew every tiny detail; and so guard would be relaxed and true information given when the interrogator slipped in the odd, vital question in a similarly casual manner.

The other technique, of swift brutality ruthlessly inflicted, is more appropriate to land warfare where instant answers to very simple questions–'Where's that bloody anti-tank gun?'–are more often required.

118

CHAPTER NINE
'Noball'
(February-August, 1944)

The shape of the future arrived in Bethnal Green, East London, on the night of 13 June, 1944. A telephone rang in the quarters of General Sir Frederick Pile, GOC-in-C of Anti-Aircraft Command. The duty Intelligence Officer was reporting the first arrival of a 'Diver', code-name for the flying bomb, the V-1.

Most people in London at that time were not aware that the night noises represented the first attack by high-tech flying robots. Indeed, as General Pile later stated, authority pretended that the V-1 was a normal bomber which had been shot down by his guns. They did this because they believed that the rest of us would panic if we were told the truth.

On 15 June there was another wave of attack, and next day the secret was out. 'Pilotless Planes Raid Southern England!' screamed the headlines. But there was no panic. Authority was wrong. Again. As they had been in the first Battle of London in 1940.

For the RAF there was no secret. The air forces had been attacking the launch sites of the German secret weapons for many months under the codename of 'Noball'. The V-1 sites were not all that vulnerable to bombing. They were just simple concrete ramps set into the London-facing edges of French woods, backed by concrete bunkers built half underground, and an immense effort had been made to destroy them. Mosquito attacks on these sites began as early as December 1943. They were not only difficult, but dangerous, often ringed by flak.

At this time Flight Lieutenant C.H.L. Foster, DFC, was flying Mosquito VIs, the fighter-bomber version, with 464 Royal Australian Air Force Squadron, part of 2 Group, now in the 2nd Tactical Air Force assigned to the Normandy campaign.

I can recall a 'Noball' op on 24 February, 1944, when the target was the usual V-1 site in France. We were based at Thorney Island, for operations in support of 'Overlord', the coming invasion. These sites were attacked by individual aircraft in daylight in the early morning at strictly timed two-minute intervals, although this procedure could be varied.

The 'form' at that time was to fly to the target at low level, getting down to really low level across the Channel and then, having crossed into France, to fly to a predetermined pin-point, climb to about 3,000 feet, spot the target, fly to it and bomb in a moderately steep dive; the bomb-load being 4 x 500 pounders with short delays. On this type of op we did not use our 20-mm cannon or machine-guns; the bombing was pilot-aimed and released.

On this occasion we were approaching the V-1 site preparatory to bombing, when we saw the crew in front of us in trouble with a damaged elevator; the aircraft went in and blew up in most dramatic fashion.

As we went down in my bombing dive and I released my bombs on the target, bits of the target came up to meet us, resulting in bricks being imbedded in the starboard wing, the bomb-doors being damaged, and our outer front windscreen being shattered–fortunately without any of it coming inwards. This reduced forward visibility to nil and a certain amount of wind came into the cockpit, to the great annoyance of my navigator, Flight Sergeant

Harold Bradley, who collected some in his face-mask. The crew I saw go in were on their first operation with 140 Wing.

One of the outstanding virtues of the Mosquito was its ability to fly on one engine. I had had proof of this earlier when, on a squadron effort on 4 February against a 'Noball' target, I had my starboard engine put out of action by flak; but apart from losing our electrics and the drop in speed, the aircraft behaved impeccably.

On another occasion, coming out of France over the Channel at low level I had a demonstration of the known fact that Mosquitos are poor 'ditchers'. A New Zealand pilot, Snowy Fittods, for some unknown reason hit the sea in what looked like an accidental ditching. I was flying a few hundred yards behind Fittods, so called to our Wing Commander, Bob Iredale, who was leading Fittods, to look behind him, which he did. The Air-Sea Rescue people were called and although Fittods was lost his navigator, Flight Sergeant Hough, survived, badly injured.

Flight Lieutenant Foster logged 84 Operations on Mosquito fighter-bombers, mostly with 2nd TAF; 11 were in daylight, 73 at night.

Most of my operations at night were against road and rail transport and installations, troop concentrations, etc., plus an intrusion now and again on enemy airfields–these were all low level using 500 lb bombs, 20mm cannon and machine-guns; also dropping flares to illuminate a possible target.

We did, however, carry out a particular type of high-level operation called GH. A few crews were trained for this, which I believe entailed a modification to the standard 'G' navigation system. I understand one idea was that we would operate when the weather was very bad and so keep the 'pot boiling', at least for 2 Group.

On 20 August, 1944 my navigator and I were detailed to carry out a GH operation at 20,000 feet over France at Duclair. The memorable part of this trip was flying up through electrically-charged clouds–the aircraft's props were like catherine wheels with the tips aglow with what I believe is called St Elmo's Fire, as were the wing-tips. The front and side screens of the aircraft were covered in electrical discharges, rather like lightning in miniature, most spectacular.

To carry out this type of op successfully the pilot had to maintain a very accurate height, course and airspeed on the bombing run, while the navigator had his eyes concentrated on the 'G' box–it was his job to release the bombs, about the only time on FB VIs that he had to do so.

Derek Bovet-White came to the Mosquito and the V-1 sites in northern France by a roundabout route. He learned to fly at Kallany in Malaya and was then posted to RAF Habbaniya in Iraq, just in time for the Rashid Ali rebellion, backed up by the Axis powers with a few aircraft, Me 110s and He 111s. This might not have been so alarming for the semi-trained British pilots to face, except for the fact that the aircraft they had to use for reconnaissance and ground-strafing was the Audax, an ancient Hawker two-seater biplane ten years out of date. For a time RAF Habbaniya was a besieged British oasis, until eventually it was relieved by the forces of Glubb Pasha's Jordanian Arab Legion. Then he and his friends were sent to Egypt for further training, and from there on to Rhodesia to learn to fly the American built Harvard trainers, 'child's play after the old Hart' (another Hawker biplane as elderly as the Audax, which it resembled).

From there the Malayan contingent split up, some volunteering for the Far East, others preferring to go to England.

Bovet-White's night-flying vision was classed 'above average' and he was posted to a squadron flying the Defiant, a single-engined two-seater fighter armed with a four-gun turret, which had been so badly treated by Adolf Galland and other crack fighter leaders of the Luftwaffe that it had been taken off daylight operations during the Battle of Britain and transferred to night-fighting duties. No sooner had Bovet-White learnt to fly the Defiant than it was pronounced obsolete at night also. He was sent to a special unit near Bournemouth flying a bewildering variety of aircraft on telecommunications duties. After one hour's experience in a Hurricane he made a take-off when the engine cut out; he broke both the Hurricane and his neck.

After three months his neck was pronounced repaired and stronger than ever, according to the Medicos. Then he got into a Spitfire and as he was coming in to land an Oxford trainer cut in on him; so, facing full into the glare of the evening sun, he had to open up his engine and attempt to go round again. He never saw the wire cable of a barrage balloon which some wily warrior had sited half-a-mile from the end of the runway, presumably to catch Stukas.

The Spitfire hit the cable with the leading edge of the wing just outside the periphery of the airscrew and, apart from the bump, I saw to my amazement that the wire was rushing down the leading edge, at great speed. I suppose it lasted for two seconds, and I had visions of the wing being cut through and a quick spiral straight down into mother earth when, fortunately, the cable broke, the balloon soared skyward, and I made the gentlest approach and most careful landing ever. The wire had cut through to the main spar. Quite obviously this non-operational flying was getting too dangerous for me and after repeated bleatings I was posted to a Mosquito intruder OTU.

Right away let it be said that the Mosquito was one of the finest twin-engined aeroplanes that has ever been made: apart from handling and aerobatic qualities which were almost as good as a single-engined fighter, she could trot along at nearly 400 mph when in a real hurry. Although constructed almost entirely of wood and plywood, I was soon to learn that this wonderful aeroplane would fly almost without visible means of support. This, coupled with the fact that my navigator who, apart from being a good Bridge player, could also navigate and interpret the complicated G-box really well, ensured that we always managed to land on a friendly aerodrome.

Early in 1944 one of the squadron's jobs was to find and destroy the V-1 ramps which the Germans were busily constructing on the north coast of France. So it was that a flight of three Mosquitos were winging their way to France on the lovely afternoon of 24 March in a nice tight vic formation at 50 feet. Leaving the south coast of England we dropped down to 20 feet over the Channel until cruising along at a happy 289 mph. Soon the coast of France loomed up in front of us, so full bore up to 3,000 feet and, weaving gently to avoid the flak, we dived down at 400 mph to 50 feet over the fields of France, heading for our target.

In less than five minutes we saw a long convoy of German lorries moving slowly along a road at right angles to our course, and almost immediately the Flight Commander's cannon and machine-guns opened fire; but I could see that most of the fire was going over the top of the lorries, so down went the nose of my Mosquito a little and, with thumb pressed hard on the firing button, much havoc and disintegration was caused amongst the German convoy as the deadly hail of bullets and cannon shells found their target. And then–crunch!

Even as the perspex cockpit-cover shattered, the starboard engine ran very roughly, and a quick glance showed masses of wire thrashing about, flaying the starboard wing, which was considerably torn and had the wing-tip missing. At one and the same time, back came the control column to gain height as quickly as possible; and the starboard propellor was feathered and the engine stopped.

My worst suspicions were then confirmed: even the French telephone wires are not much more than 20 feet up–and we had certainly managed to sever telephonic communications in this part of France.

Fortunately, the Rolls Royce Merlin on the port side was still singing a joyous song of power, but the Mosquito was vibrating quite a bit, with jagged pieces of the starboard wing flapping in most un-aerofoil fashion. Using almost full throttle on the port engine we were just making 170 mph; and once, when speed dropped to 160, we almost fell out of the sky. Obviously, we only had 10 mph above the new, unorthodox stalling speed of the reshaped Mosquito. But even as we approached the French coast, heading for home as fast as we could, the German light flak started.

We let the two 500 lb, 11 seconds-delay bombs go with a satisfactory *wump-wump;* but these did not seem to discourage the German flak very much, so down went the Mosquito's nose again and, weaving rapidly at 200 mph, we dived down to the English Channel. Occasionally, there would be a noise like hailstones on a tin roof, but mostly the flak was blazing on one side or the other and quite soon it stopped. Then we had the serious business of getting to England in one piece.

A quick check showed that Beachy Head was the nearest bit of England and Friston, a Spitfire aerodrome, was very close by. So, steering a steady course and climbing all we could, which in fact was about 50 feet a minute, we vibrated our way to England. The port engine was taking a beating, running almost at full bore, and the oil and water temperatures were rising higher and higher, but at long last beautiful Beachy Head came into view.

Obviously, the landing would have to be made at 165 mph, which is 50 mph faster than normal, and we were going to cover a lot of the grass area at Friston before stopping, but I decided to give it a try.

As we made a circuit I let the wheels down, although the flaps refused to lower, and, settling down to a steady 165 mph, I lined up for the grassy strip.

We were certainly moving, and as we touched down it seemed obvious that we were quickly going to run straight off the end at Friston and fall 175 feet off the cliffs into the sea, despite all the brakes could do. So off with the fuel-tap and up with the undercarriage-lever, and the tattered Mosquito sank on her belly and scuffed to an untidy halt. As my navigator and I jumped out of the Mossy as quickly as possible, we realised that there were still 200 yards to go to the cliff edge, but a quick look at the noble old lady showed that she would never have flown again anyway. The fuselage and tailplane were riddled with holes, the starboard wing was torn in dozens of places, and one wondered how she managed to stay in the sky.

They told us at the hilarious party in the mess that evening, that we had brought back 150 feet of French telephone wire with us.

During the invasion period of June and July Derek Bovet-White once tried to catch a V-1 speeding over the battlefront at Villers Bocage. 'I tried but I couldn't–they did about 425 mph and we about 400.' But he helped burn a train believed to be carrying V-1s. On 1 August, 1944 he took part in one of those spectacular daylight low-level pin-point attacks, some of which–like the raid on Amiens prison–became famous. This time the target was a German barracks east of Poitiers, attacked by 24 Mosquitos from 487 and 21 Squadrons. Bovet-White's bomb hung up and his aircraft sustained bird damage, but the attack generally he thought 'magnificent'. Barracks, however, unlike Gestapo prisons, were not exciting enough for the media, even though completely and accurately gutted as this one was; so, while Amiens became a classic story, other, equally brilliant strikes, remain unknown.

The V-1 was, of course, a jet; and the Mosquito had lost its speed advantage, although efforts were made to boost performance at the heights at which the robot-planes flew–2,000–3,000 feet–an area not well overlapped by the various types of AA gun. Jeremy Howard-Williams, of the experimental Fighter Interception Unit, wrote.

Mosquitos engaged in the anti-*Diver* role were usually the Mark XIX, low-level aircraft fitted with Merlin 25s. Exhaust-flame dampers were removed and the engines boosted to give +24-lb boost with 150 octane fuel. The nose sections had to be strengthened to withstand the effects of cannon fire at such high speeds. The usual system was for the Mosquito to patrol at about 8,000 feet (2,000 ft higher than the faster Tempest had to go) if the weather were clear enough, so that it had 5,000–6,000 ft advantage on the flying bomb; it could then increase speed in the dive and try to destroy its target before entering the AA gun belt. The guns by now were extremely lethal, for they were using proximity fuses which meant that any shells which passed near a solid object exploded as soon as they got close enough. So even a near miss could bring down an aircraft as easily as a flying bomb.

Now the robot bomber was being countered by the robot shell. And behind the gun-line lay the balloon line. Like the guns, many of these sites were 'manned' by women. At this time, Sylvia Cane was a WAAF on a balloon site protecting London, and although the defending fighters were supposed to stay out of the gun and balloon areas, her balloon could, had it wished, have claimed a Mosquito destroyed.

When the V-1s were battering London I was stationed at Plumstead. Our balloon was flying at 1,500 feet, and suddenly a Mosquito ran into the cable–about 18 inches of its wing–tip landed near our site. We were very worried for the pilot's safety. However, about two or three hours later the CO from his station told us the pilot was OK. You can guess, when we went to the local that night, what a reception we got. They wanted to know if we were on Göring's side or ours!

After the mishap with the Mosquito, we had to find our balloon, or what was left of it, so we made our way to the area where it was last seen coming down. When we got there, to our surprise, it was cordoned off. We were told by the Police that a landmine was on the roof of a building and they were waiting for the Army to defuse it.

You can imagine what relief they felt–among other emotions–when we told them it was our deflated balloon up there and not the parachute of a landmine.

The secret of the guarded hangar – De Havilland's Mosquito, the most versatile aircraft of the Second World War. This is a late Night Fighter Mark with improved radar in the bulbous nose.

Coster collection

WITHDRAWN

The men who designed the Mosquito. *David King collection*

The sandbagged entrance to Salisbury Hall in 1940. *Goldsmith collection*

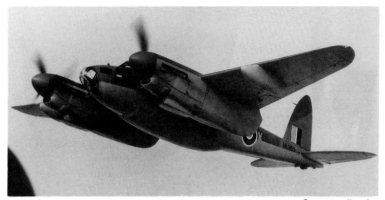

Coster collection

Coster collection

Coster collection

The Mosquito PR XV1 photo-recce version. *McCreith collection*

Anzac Day, 25 April, 1944 – crews of 464 Squadron, RAAF, just before take-off for a 'Noball' operation. C. H. L. Foster is fourth from left. *Foster collection*

A 4,000-lb thin-walled 'cookie' being loaded into the modified bomb-bay of a Mosquito. *Nunn collection*

The official send-off from Benson for the attempt to fly to Buenos Aires in a day, 22 September, 1946. *Left to right:* F/Lt S. McCreith (wearing an observer-type chute for greater comfort on a long flight); Aire Commodore MacDonald (AOC Benson), F/Lt F. E. Thayer, and a G/Cp from Air Ministry.   *DH photo in McCreith collection*

Mosquito PR 34 ready to leave Benson for the Argentine.
DH photo in McCreith collection

Last operational flight of an RAF Mosquito, 81 Squadron.
Left, F/O 'Tommy' Thompson (nav), with F/O 'Collie' Knox (pilot), 15 December, 1955.
McCreith collection

Engine start for the last op from RAF Seletar, Singapore, by a PR 34 of 81 Squadron.
McCreith collection

Line-up of Israeli
Mosquitos commanded by
Colonel Easterman,
27 April, 1956.
Easterman collection

Ground crew at work,
27 April, 1956.
Easterman collection

Engine overhaul, 27 April, 1956.   *Easterman collection*

We had to laugh at all the excitement we had caused, and then it was back to the site to inflate a new balloon.

Sylvia Cane was never told whether the Mosquito crew had bailed out or had been able to land their machine, minus part of its wing. Derek Bovet-White who, as we know, had survived a balloon cable collision in a Spitfire, rather favoured the Mosquito as far as gunfire was concerned:

The Mosquito was less susceptible to damage than a metal aircraft. Instead of bending metal, it just punched a hole right through the structure.

Flying low over the battle area, Bovet-White's log briefly chronicled the change of fortune. On 18 August, for instance, he noted: 'Big German retreat. Bombed vehicles in Lisieux-Rouen area.' His entry for 25 August read: 'Rouen in flames. Terrific explosions.' This was victory. Germany had certainly lost the war. The race for the Rhine was on.

CHAPTER TEN
Bomber Support (1943-1945)

The ground-crew help me up the flimsy collapsible metal ladder into the entrance hatch on the starboard side of the nose, and I squeeze myself through the small opening. I am a trifle nervous, and the cramped cockpit and my bulky flying clothes, Mae West and parachute make the process ungainly and sweaty. I fall back into the pilot's seat and let out a puff of breath as I grope for the unfamiliar straps. The airman helping me grunts as he pulls the shoulder straps over.

'Don't worry, sir', he grins. 'They say a Mossie's like a virgin: difficult to get into but lovely when you're there.'

Jeremy Howard-Williams in his book 'Night Intruder'

By 1944 the initially unwanted Mosquito had been required to perform in a bewildering variety of roles. Some of these arose from the growing successes of the German defences against Bomber Command and the four-engined heavies. A combination of electronics, night-fighters, radar directed searchlights and predicted flak had begun to inflict unbearable losses. So the Mosquitos–which suffered few losses–were called in to help. Firstly for accurate target-marking, carried out low down with precision. Secondly, for 'spoof' raids, intended to draw the German night-fighters away from the real targets for the night. Thirdly, by intruding over German night-fighter bases and trying to shoot down anything which took off or landed. Fourthly, in a version packed with radar, virtually to escort the bomber stream, picking up the German nightfighters and then picking them off. And, fifthly, by taking over part of the bombing job– sending out large formations consisting of Mosquitos only.

Jeremy Howard-Williams who, after completing his first tour with 604 Squadron, joined the experimental Fighter Interception Unit (FIU) stationed at Ford in Sussex, flew a Mosquito on an early bomber support operation. This was to Hanover on 16 October, 1943. 'Uneventful' was the entry he made in his log book.

He had a bumpy climb to 20,000 feet, largely in cloud, which he described in his book *Night Intruder:*

Soon we were flying on DR only, until ahead of us we could see redness glowing dully through the overcast. As we approached, the red area separated into individual fires which, on yet closer investigation, flared up through gaps in the clouds. We could see the shock of individual bomb loads exploding on the ground as the city of Hanover was systematically taken apart in an awesome demonstration of the destructive power of a modern air force. Bursts of flak speckled the sky over the target area and occasionally a flaming torch was lit as a bomber fell earthwards, cut down by flak or the night-fighters.

We flew all round the edge of the target, with Mac searching the *Monica* rear warner and the AI for signs of the enemy, until the last aircraft headed for home; all we saw was our own bombers. Fires continued to rage below us and could still be seen long after we had turned for base. I thrust into the back of my mind all thought of the misery and suffering going on below us as we concentrated on the return journey, checking off landmarks and enemy light beacons on the way out. I sweated like a bull for the entire trip and arrived back wringing wet. Uneventful indeed!

John Jacobs flew Mosquito FB IVS from 1944 to 1945 with 23 Squadron, part of 100 (Bomber Support) Group. Some units of the group flew escorts with the stream, seeking German night-fighters, while others jammed German radar.

23 Squadron was a low-level intruder squadron, operating usually from nought to 2,000 feet. We were equipped with the Mosquito Fighter-Bomber Mk IV, fitted with 'Ash' and Perfectos and Gee. 'Ash' was an American ASV-type radar adapted by us to serve as AI with a twin-tube display. It was contained in a torpedo-shaped unit fitted in the nose of the aircraft in place of the four Browning .303 guns. Perfectos was a device for homing on enemy night-fighter transmissions. Some said *they* found it useful to locate *our* presence.

At briefing the squadron was given times, targets and routes of the bomber force. Each intruder crew was allotted a target of an enemy night-fighter base to be patrolled. Nearly all such bases were patrolled in order not to give the enemy any clue as to where the main attack force was heading. Each crew worked out their own dog-leg courses and times to arrive at their station exactly on time, and had to leave dead on time, because if more than one Mosquito was in an enemy circuit at one time they would be stalking each other. Ammunition had to be reserved for engaging enemy aircraft in their circuit. On the way home we were free to attack anything we saw. Trains and road transport were the usual targets. The enemy often had dummy flare paths alight near their bases to confuse us, but we had studied charts of the real airfields and were not usually fooled. The aerodrome buildings were strafed before we left if there was not too much flak opposition.

On nights when Bomber Command did not need support we conducted our private war with individual low-level 'Ranger' patrols—a five-hour dog-leg

132

tour between German towns, attacking trains or anything that moved.

One night in 1945 the squadron mounted its own attack on the airfield of Munich/Reim. The squadron commander acted as Master Bomber and stood by directing the rest of us (about ten aircraft) where to strafe and drop our bombs. After the war, we learned that one of the first Me 262 jet squadrons was there under the command of Colonel Tohannes Steinhoff (later a NATO general commanding the West German air force). I corresponded with him and he remembered the night and said that we had destroyed most of his aircraft on the ground. Only once did we attack a German jet. We got behind one on its approach to Burg (the German Farnborough). Their flak defences were reacting violently. We claimed him damaged as we did not see him hit the ground. Most of our squadron's successes were against Ju 88s.

We regarded ourselves as very privileged to be flying Mosquitos. It was a match for any enemy, the only faster prop. aircraft being the FW 190. I have seen aircraft terribly damaged by flak and by hitting objects on the ground–but they flew back to base.

Raymond H. Smith, a warrant officer pilot, held the same opinion, after equally extensive experience.

I flew the Mosquito in most of its wartime marks, operationally as night-intruder pilot with 605 (County of Warwick) Squadron based at Ford in Sussex, Castle Camps and Manston in Kent, and later as a test and ferry pilot with 151 Repair Unit (Aircraft) of 2nd TAF based at B55 Courtai/ Wevelgem in Belgium.

There was something most exciting about night-intruder ops carried out at very low level in all weathers. Sea crossings were made under radar cover literally at 50 feet and then lone flights, not often above 2,000 feet, to selected enemy airfields. A typical flight through predicted searchlights and flak belts would be carried out by dead reckoning and map reading of such prominent features as rivers and canals, and inside Germany by accurate location of large lakes such as the Dümmersee near Osnabrück and Steinhuder Meer near Hanover. The 'Gee' box navigational aid, useful for returning to base in bad weather, was usually jammed or out-ranged at low level over Germany. Sheer speed carried the Mosquito through most trouble spots, unlike the high-flying bomber stream carefully threading its way at 20,000 feet by routes avoiding known 'hot' areas.

In my opinion the most successful aspect of 'intruding' was the considerable panic caused at German night-fighter bases by the presence of a Mosquito on the circuit. Runways kept doused, local and diverted enemy aircraft low in fuel often unable to land. Mosquitos beating up airfields and if possible bombing runways made German night-fighter operations hazardous at all times. A procession of Mosquitos visiting German bases all over Holland, France and Germany—especially those in the vicinity of the 'target for tonight'—aided most effectively the safer progress of bomber streams to and from their target. Although I was never able to score even a probable myself, many German night-fighters were shot down on landing and take-off runs by an intruder lucky enough to surprise them in the act.

To prove his point, Raymond Smith lent me a copy of a friend's logbook. This crew had been luckier, in one way, than Smith, in finding German aircraft in a vulnerable position. They carried out a great many operations in the summer of 1943. On 12 June they went to Twente/Enschede on the border of Holland and Germany and caught an aircraft on the approach, its belly-light flashing.

An interception was made just before the enemy aircraft touched down. Fire was opened from 60 degrees beam from 400 yards at 200 feet. A burst of two to three seconds was fired and bullets were seen bursting but whether on the ground or on the enemy aircraft it was impossible to say as the enemy aircraft was touching down. All lights doused as the attack opened. Only one cannon fired, but all .303 fired satisfactorily.

Only a few days later, on 15 June, they went to an airfield at Aalborg West.

This was found lit up with normal red perimeter lighting and several obstruction lights, especially in Aalborg town itself, together with the NW/SE runway, at the North end of which was a long line of Lorenz. Patrol was started at 200 feet about four to five miles from the aerodrome at 00.30 hours and after making one complete orbit and starting a second, an enemy aircraft was sighted burning green and white navigation lights, taking off. Turned to starboard and gained height to 2,000 feet for a stern attack, and closing to 200 yards the pilot opened fire at 00. 45 hours giving a two to three second burst of machine-gun and cannon. After one second, strikes were seen on the starboard engine and fuselage and the port engine caught fire. The enemy aircraft glided down with the fire spreading to the fuselage and was seen to crash and blow up about seven miles West of Aalborg West aerodrome . . . No flak or searchlights encountered throughout the patrol. Claims: One He 177 destroyed.

There followed a number of nights when aerodrome traffic was disturbed, but on 17 July there was more promising activity at Venlo, on the Dutch border.

Target reached at 00.45 hours, and 500 feet. Two large fires were seen in Venlo. Dummy went on and off, and at 02.15 hours the aerodrome lit up. A weak searchlight at the North West end of runway was depressed and elevated quickly several times and at 02.32 hours the flarepath came on, and perimeter lighting. At 02.35 hours a green was fired from the aerodrome but as patrol had finished, course was set at 02.36 hours. At 02.44 hours Eindhoven was seen alight and at 02.47 hours an enemy aircraft with navigation lights on was seen and chased cross-wind prior to landing, at which enemy aircraft doused navigation lights to flash them periodically every five or ten seconds. The position of enemy aircraft was judged to be going down visual Lorenz but on putting on its lights it was found they had overshot. This enemy aircraft landed and at 02.51 hours another enemy aircraft with navigation lights was seen in the circuit. Chase was given down-wind at 02.54 hours when 150 yards astern a two-second burst of cannon and machine-gun was given and return fire from dorsal turret. Strikes were seen on fuselage and starboard engine which burst into flames. The enemy aircraft made a diving turn to port, crashed and burst into flames at 02.55 hours, approximately four miles North East of visual Lorenz. The attack was made at 1,500 feet, our aircraft breaking away to port and the Observer maintains that he saw two parachutes come out as the engine exploded.

Night after night they went out with results not so spectacular, but nevertheless efficiently dislocating to German night-fighter operations. The names of some of their targets were most familiar to me, although I saw them in different circumstances. Beauvais in France . . . sitting in a British Army vehicle while German soldiers, guarded by armed Frenchmen of the FFI, were herded past. Eindhoven in Holland . . . that was where they made the torches which did not need batteries (virtually unobtainable then). Paderborn . . . burnt-out Mark IVs (Panzers, not Mosquitos!) where a training school had made a desperate last stand. On 15 September they went to Melun and Bretigny in France. They passed several airfields with activity going on, but no real targets, so returned for another look at Melun. The flarepath was lit up, red at its western end, green at the eastern.

When on the southern side of the aerodrome, an enemy aircraft was seen to take off with aircraft recognition lights GG. Our aircraft turned in passing over the perimeter, when three guns and two searchlights attempted to engage and the enemy aircraft put out its lights. Continued along the visual Lorenz and obtained a visual, the enemy aircraft turning to starboard. Closed to 100 yards, dead astern, at 1,000 feet and gave a one-second burst. Strikes were seen, fire breaking out in the gondola, and the enemy aircraft, a Do 217, crashed, exploding with a brilliant orange flame: and an extra run was made, exposing camera, the enemy aircraft burning for twenty minutes. Many flashes, as of ammunition exploding, were seen going off and later, two stationary lights were seen, as of car headlamps. The target area was left at 23.15 hours. On the way out, two large fires, as of crashed aircraft, were seen east of Abbeville/Drucat. At 23.44 hours a train at Moyenville was attacked but no conclusive results were observed.

Although Raymond Smith was not so successful in shooting down enemy aircraft, his operations were not without excitement.

Strong squadron morale helped to take in our stride the many sleepless nights (Squadron Motto–*Nunquam Dormio*) and little frights like crossing out from enemy territory at nought feet to the merry tones of the Freya and Wurzburg radars on the R/T as they still vainly searched for those demmed elusive Mosquitos. Not so clever on one occasion when a navigational hiccough meant haring through the docks at Antwerp–the cranes silhouetted above the aircraft in crossbeam searchlights as the flak banged away!

On another night in 1943 we were hit by predicted flak while patrolling over unlit St Trond airfield. The port wing took a right beating; hydraulic lines breached meant undercarriage, flaps and brakes all u/s. Back at base my navigator pumped down the wheels with the emergency system and we made a long run in. One of the joys of the Mosquito was the grand straight bore-in it always made of the landing run. Even in atrocious conditions my superb Mk VI FB, HJ784, made a perfect night landing returning to Castle Camps in September 1943, by using two vertical searchlights, Fido paraffin burning, and a brilliant green, white and red runway lighting system known as Piccadilly Circus.

Another night-fighter pilot who had occasion to mention St Trond in his logbook was Hauptmann Paul Zorner of III Gruppe, NJG5, stationed at Mainz-Finthen. His aircraft was a Messerschmidt 110G-4 and the date was 21 April, 1944.

During the night of 20–21 April the RAF attacked Köln. I know that I took off from Finthen at 01.39 hours and flew north-west to meet the bombers. It is possible that we received our orders too late; certainly I did not arrive over Köln until towards the end of the attack at 02.20 hours. If I remember correctly, the weather was relatively bad, with thick cloud at various levels. We searched the area west of Köln but found ourselves constantly diving into cloud.

Towards 02.40 hours my wireless-operator found a target on a westerly course, which on our weak SN2 apparatus gave only a faint zig-zag signal. Therefore we assumed at first that this was one of our own night-hunters. As there was nothing else of interest, we decided to follow this target. The plane was flying calmly on an almost exactly west course at an altitude of 4,000 metres. We were in a cloud layer and visibility was very bad.

We slowly closed up to our target from behind and below, and at 02.50 hours I sighted, less than 200 metres away, a twin-engined plane. Obviously, a German night-hunter after all.

Looking more closely, however, I realised that it was neither an Me 110 nor a Ju 88. The plane looked like a Mosquito, but seemed to fly too slowly for such an aircraft. I moved up closer and, from approximately 50 metres away, saw that the propellor of the left-hand motor was not turning. It was clear to me that this must be an English plane trying to get home on one motor.

I therefore attacked at 03.00 hours and fired from less than 50 metres into the right-hand motor. The shots were well placed and the plane keeled over, right wing down, and disappeared in the mist. We circled for a while and noted a flash and then a fire at 03.06 hours, down below. Our position was

30–40 kilometres south-west of Antwerp.

At 03.15 hours we landed at St Trond and reported enemy-engagement. The next morning the crash of a Mosquito north-west of St Trond was confirmed. I flew this particular Me 110 from December 1943 to the beginning of July 1944, and with it achieved 42 victories.

Zorner's total number of victories was 59; but this was the only Mosquito, the *Sperrholz* (plywood) *Bomber*, as he called it, was far too fast to be caught under normal circumstances.

The 6th of June, 1944 triggered a process which, within four months, was to alter the balance of the war in the air (and under the sea). The invasion of Normandy, which began that day, was to deprive Germany of all France, all Belgium and half Holland–the forward air defences of the Reich, from the fighter airfields to the radar warning systems, were forced back almost to the Rhine.

On the evening of invasion day, Jeremy Howard-Williams was flying a low-level intruder over the new battlefield in France. He damaged a Heinkel 177, but his thoughts were with the soldiers below him. In his diary he wrote:

They must be sweating it out down there and many on both sides will be dying. Not for the first time I reflect upon my good fortune at not having to slog it out with the army, creeping forward through mud and rubble expecting death at every hedgerow and street corner . . . the deadly game of hide and seek. We at least are slightly more masters of our own fate and are remote from the immediate din and shock of battle. We do our fighting sitting down and come back to a bath and clean sheets. I am certain that this is the only way I could play an honourable part in this nightmare . . .

Raymond Smith, having finished a tour of operations, went into Europe with 2nd TAF once the breakout from the beach-head had begun towards the end of August.

Mobile repair crews were sent out by lorry to remote airfields to repair aircraft which had force-landed or been abandoned. Many were Mosquitos in varying conditions of unserviceability and neglect. It says a great deal for their design and construction that we were able to rescue, service, test and ferry to UK-based MUs a large number of aircraft that otherwise might have been written off. I recall bringing back from Y29 (Asch in Belgium) a Mk XXX Mosquito, MM818. It had lain there unattended for three months, flak-damaged. It flew violently left-wing low and dropped boost and revs. on port engine which had a magnificent oil leak spurting the low-grade Yankee oil perforce used. Yet when this same aircraft came out of the hangar at Courtrai B55 after a major service and a spanking new paint job, it was as good as new. I ferried it then to RAF Edzell, near Dundee, which was handy as I lived in Perth!

Other reclaimed Mosquitos suffered from fungus growth in the tail unit to varying degrees. None ever dropped off on me and it is true to say that in years of almost daily (sometimes nightly) flying, not one Mosquito I flew ever suffered a total engine failure. The whole aircraft when correctly serviced exuded reliability and was always a joy to fly. Its wooden construction may have been sneered at but this very unorthodoxy, in my view, enabled it to survive flak damage since in most cases objects passed straight through it–and the pilot had a magnificent chunk of armour-plating behind him. Speed and manoeuvrability

141

were increased by the balsa and plywood lightweight construction. It was just a superb fighting machine.

The only faults I can remember were a tendency for its glycol-cooled engines to overheat when taxiing, a cockpit full of smoke when the cannons fired, and an inclination–easily corrected–to swing to starboard when taking off and landing.

Occasions when a Mosquito broke up in the air were rare. Flying Officer R.G. Pickles, of 25 Squadron, stationed then at Castle Camps, witnessed an exception.

That Mossie hadn't been on an op, just a night-flying test. The pilot was a new boy, and there was a rise in the centre of the airfield. He was beating up the airfield, misjudged, pulled up far too sharp, and that was it. We all felt on the squadron that the structure of the aircraft was first class. In fact, I've seen pilots roll the thing with all that equipment aboard, at altitude, mind you. Not me, though.

Pickles also flew bomber support missions to German airfields. On 17 October, 1944, when the Allied offensive on the continent had been halted on the river lines of Holland, he was sent to Recklin. What the Germans made of it, he never learned.

The port engine after-burners disintegrated and the flames from my exhaust stubs looked like the jet engine of a V-1. So I soon shut down and returned on one engine, very smooth.

Already, on 13 October, 1944, the first V-2 supersonic rockets had begun to fall into Antwerp, a few hours after King George VI and Field Marshal Montgomery had inspected the unit I was with. We guessed they were rockets from the nature of the craters they made, but the whole thing, both in England and on the continent was, as usual, kept very hush-hush for fear of frightening the horses, I suppose. On the night of 24 October, Flying Officer Pickles was out intruding over the Arnhem area of Holland, when he tried to catch one, not realising what it was.

> Knowing nothing of the V-2 in those early days, I saw one launched, one of the first ones. Intelligence hadn't warned us on the Squadron, so, not knowing what it was but thinking it appeared to be aimed at us–this ball of flame–I was automatically following it with the sight, not realising that I was pulling the nose up. The aircraft stalled, very unpleasant, but I pulled out, took a fix for when we returned but heard no more.

The full beauty of this story cannot be realised by anyone who has not seen a V-2 launched (although American space probes give the general idea). They rose from the ground almost vertically, accelerating rapidly to well beyond the speed of sound and on and on, up and up into the stratosphere before arcing over to Antwerp, Liege or London. Being as inaccurate as the V-1, their military value was slight, but they were an illuminating introduction to the wars of the future. V-1 could be caught, just, and was vulnerable to AA fire also, but against V–2 there was no defence–and no warning of its arrival. However, on 16 September, 1944, Jeremy Howard-Williams, on an intruder op to Gütersloh and Paderborn, very nearly became the first–and only–man to shoot one down. In his published diary he wrote:

> As we cross in just north of the Hague, we see a white flame pulsing at ground level and, because nobody has told us that V-2s don't take off with a rush like a child's firework rocket, we don't realise

143

what we are looking at. They have only been coming over for about a week and are still rather strange and secret. A pity, because we were in a perfect position to have a shot at it and it would have been nice to be able to say that we had shot down a V-2, not to mention the saving of life in England.

Howard-Williams was critical of the Bomber Command set-up they were supporting. As a member of Fighter Command's experimental unit, it was his business to look for weak points. And Bomber Command had plenty, in spite of–or often because of–the complicated staff work which lay behind the mass raids. The first proof of what was happening was provided by a Ju 88 which landed by mistake at Woodbridge in Suffolk on 13 July, 1944; it was full of electronic equipment.

Derek Jackson, now a wing commander, conducted flying trials which proved conclusively to Air Marshal Harris that German night-fighters could home onto his bombers on their *Monica* transmissions alone. Harris's reaction was characteristic and immediate. He ordered the removal of *Monica* from all his aircraft and, alert at last to the dangers of too many transmissions, instructed his crews not to switch on their H2S until they were within enemy radar coverage, nor to use their IFF unless in distress. The stable door was now shut.

Bomber Command had the most extraordinarily tight security on the Stations when a raid was impending, foolproof against your conventional spy, had he in fact existed, which seems doubtful, but were apparently unaware that the Germans had long been monitoring British radio transmissions–for five years, at least.

It seems incredible with hindsight that our aircraft

could have been allowed to go on so long, not only advertising their presence in the air but, through test transmissions both from the ground and in the air during the day, giving warning of their intentions when there was to be an attack in the evening. The German interception service monitored our radio ground stations as W/T equipment was tested during the morning, noted increased aerial activity during the day as aircraft were tested in the air, picked up H2S transmissions from the bomber stream as soon as it left the English coast, and cross-checked this tracking by interrogating the bombers' IFF sets. Night-fighters took off and proceeded to trigger our IFF, home onto H2S and *Monica* transmissions and then make their interceptions with SN2, using *Lichtenstein* for the final stages if the former proved incapable of bringing the target near enough for the pilot to get a visual. Attack was finally made from the relative invisibility and security of a position well below the target, by means of *Schräge Musik*, the upward-firing guns. It was scientific slaughter, largely made possible by the very aids which the authorities piled into the unsuspecting bombers.

Luckily, the Germans made errors just as great. Hitler, in particular, obsessed with attack when defence was the only sane course, ordered the new German jet fighters to be converted into bombers; in the resulting chaos, Germany got neither the one nor the other in any numbers.

That slaughter would have been far worse had it not been for the 'bomber support' missions carried out mainly by Mosquitos. That these were brilliantly successful is confirmed by their direct opponents on the German side. One of them, Hauptmann H. Rökker of I Gruppe NJG2, scored a rare victory over a Mosquito on 17 March, 1945, by using the same intruder tactics as they did with his slower Junkers J 88 G-6 over an Allied aerodrome in Belgium or Holland.

This was only possible because the Mosquito was at the fringe of the aerodrome, with extended under-carriage and all the navigation lights blazing, ready to land. It was–incidentally–my last hit; and, fortunately, my only involvement with a Mosquito.

Our most dangerous adversaries were not the bombers with their gunners but the long-distance night-fighters. Because of them we suffered heavy losses in 1944 at our aerodromes, especially when taking-off or landing. Owing to their speed and more advanced radar, the performance of the Mosquito crews was superior to our own.

Also, during our attacks on bomber formations our crews sometimes became the victims of the British night-hunters. Some crews of my own unit were shot down by English night-hunters. There-fore, we became very much aware of the potency of our enemies and felt–towards the end of the war–that we were the hunted, not the hunters. We had to try to keep the 'competition' at a distance by constantly changing altitude and direction.

As our Ju 88 and Me 110 were too slow, specially-equipped night-hunter aircraft were introduced in action against the Mosquitos. These used the Me 109, the Me 219 and lastly, the Me 262. But those planes were combined in special units with which we had no contact at all. At the time, we regretted very much that no machines of equivalent capability were available to us.

But, as we shall see, the Focke-Wulf 190 was also used, sometimes with success, against Mosquitos at night.

An interesting viewpoint by one witness who, although not on the German side, was on the receiving end of

Allied bombing, was John O. Millham, a navigator with the USAAF 457th Bomb Group, equipped with B-17 Flying Fortresses, who was shot down and wounded on 28 May, 1944, just before D-Day. His subsequent experiences convinced him that 'the Mosquito was one of the most effective planes in WWII'.

I was taken to a Catholic hospital in Bremen, where I stayed for two months before being sent on to a prison hospital. This hospital, the St Joseph Stiftus, was equipped with a bunker larger than the hospital. In air raids, time allowing, all the patients were moved into the bunker and hospital services, including surgery, were continued without interruption.

The first floor of the bunker was available to anyone in the neighbourhood. To get into it, on the first floor, all these people (soldiers, sailors, generals, admirals, housewives, children, patients, etc) had to go through the area set aside for Allied POWs such as I.

In the case of the B-17s, B-24s, Lancasters, Stirlings, there was plenty of warning–sometimes hours–and the move into the bunker was very well organised and calm. If there was time, the bedridden prisoners were taken in.

This was not so in the case of a Mosquito raid. The bombs would be dropping before the alarms were sounded. Bedlam erupted. People in all stages of fright and attire would come streaming through, trampling each other. It would be impossible to move the patients and surgical procedures would be interrupted. These were the only times during my imprisonment that I saw any real signs of demoralisation among the Germans (military and civilian).

It seems ironic that the four-motor 'heavies' which the bomber chiefs had calculated would produce a panic

flight on the part of the civilian population, largely failed
to do so; but that the light, cheap Mosquito, crewed by
only two men, actually did have an effect on morale.

CHAPTER ELEVEN
Pathfinders
(1944-1945)

We had a few of these bomber Mosquitos which nobody wanted, but which had been ordered in a small test order by the Ministry of Aircraft Production. They had no armament of any sort, but were indeed very fast little craft. They had a bomb bay big enough to take four of our five-hundred-pound Target Indicators, and it seemed to me that if they could achieve the ceiling we required they would be perfectly suitable. At a meeting at the Air Ministry on the subject, Bomber Command and the Air Ministry both very strongly opposed the adoption of the Mosquito. They argued that it was a frail wood machine totally unsuitable for Service conditions, that it would be shot down because of the absence of gun turrets, and that in any case it was far too small to carry the equipment and an adequate Pathfinder crew. I dealt with each one of these points in turn, but finally they played their ace. They declared that the Mosquito had been tested thoroughly by the appropriate establishments and found quite unsuitable, and indeed impossible to fly at night. At this I raised an eyebrow, and said that I was very sorry to hear that it was quite impossible to fly it by night, as I had been doing so regularly during the past week and had found nothing wrong. There was a deathly silence. I got my Mosquitos.
Air Vice-Marshal D. C. T. Bennett in his book, 'Pathfinder'

The idea of using the Mosquito for marking instead of the slow and ponderous Lancasters occurred to a number of people at various times, now hard to pin-point because neither they nor their biographers are generous with dates; and internal RAF politics played a part also. The official Pathfinder Force was commanded by Air Vice-Marshal Bennett, a forthright Australian who, unlike most other senior RAF commanders, insisted on flying operations with his men in a private Beaufighter of his own, 'breathing down their necks' as one of them put it. Bennett also controlled the meteorological Mosquitos of 1409 Flight, which checked on the weather over enemy territory.

Gradually a rival pathfinder force came into being, based originally on the 'Dam Busting' Squadron, 617, who were very proud of their accuracy. (They, too, have been criticised for losing seven out of their 18 Lancasters during their fly-in at low level to the dams, a very high loss-rate compared to the Mosquito). Group Captain Cheshire, who took over in succession to Guy Gibson, came to the conclusion that the accurate marking of targets for the main force heavy bombers was best done in a shallow dive from a fast Mosquito operating at low level, and managed to convince his own commander, Ralph Cochrane of 5 Group. There are various stories of how he wangled a couple of Mosquitos out of Harris, the head of Bomber Command and a convinced exponent of the heavy four-motor bomber. For his part, Cheshire was critical of the standard attack method. 'Everything was wound up and pre-set like an alarm clock hundreds of miles from a target, as though all the unknown factors could be predetermined infallibly and the raid conducted by the remote control of unseen experts'. The result of such thoughts was the creation, under Cochrane's command, of a system of Master Bombers who had some powers of control actually on the battlefield, so to speak (although Harris retained overall command from his control post deep underground at High Wycombe).

Leonard Cheshire was awarded his VC for the Munich raid of 24 April, 1944, when, leading four Mosquitos, he marked the target at 500 feet for the main force, which has been held to be a landmark in technique.

This is the essential background to the formation of the Light Night Striking Force, which consisted entirely of Mosquito bombers to the number of 70 or 80, which provided their own pathfinders, also in Mosquitos. In most cases, their task was to pose an alternative threat to lure away from the vulnerable 'heavies' of the main force a significant proportion of the German night-fighters. Sometimes, instead of 'spoofing', they were 'jamming', to create more confusion for the German fighter controllers. One of those who flew as pathfinder for this force was Alan J. A. Woollard of 139 (Jamaica) Squadron from 8 Group.

After a six-month tour with 106 Squadron on Lancasters, followed by a year with 29 OTU teaching navigation to Wellington crews, the change to Mosquitos when I joined 139 (Jamaica) Squadron was remarkable. It was equivalent to being transferred from heavy goods vehicles to the Williams racing team. At the Mosquito conversion unit the art of precise navigation was stressed. It followed that with accurate windfinding and correct interpretation, dead-reckoning navigation enabled targets to be located well beyond the range of 'Gee'. And this was necessary, as to start with 139's aircraft were not equipped with H2S. In fact bombing was done with the then obsolete CSBS (Course Setting Bomb Sight).

My first eight Mosquito operations were really in the nature of nuisance raids but it was surprising the ease with which the targets were located. Possibly the trip I best remember was the very first Mosquito operation to Schweinfurt. I should think that more important than actually bombing the town was the job of pouring out many bundles of 'Window' over the target. A main force heavy raid was about five or ten minutes behind us and we had to obscure the German radar screens with the metal foil. And as we made our third run over the town, the raid started up. We were fascinated to watch the heavies running in many thousands of feet below.

Thus far, the squadron was operating in a support role for the heavy bombers. Then came a change of equipment and of plan.

I was now sent on a concentrated course to Newmarket to learn H2S, and returned to 139 to a Mossie that had the gubbins fitted. All trips were now marker trips, marking the targets for the other Mosquito squadrons; and these Mossie raids were developed to a fine art. Markers went down right on time, accurately placed, and the whole raid was over in some ten minutes; sometimes less. *En route* to the target the Force was kept well bunched by the PFF aircraft at the front firing Verey cartridges of an agreed colour or dropping flares or ground markers.

It is important to realise that Mossie raids were tied in with the raids of the main force; and it was the Mossies' job to fill the sky with 'window', pretend to be the main force, and to attract the German night-fighters away from the true target. On many trips we had fighter flares all around us, so it was obvious our efforts were worthwhile.

Undoubtedly the trip most to be remembered was my last one. On 11 June, 1944, Berlin was the target and we received a very rough reception. We were adopting the tactic of marking, and then nosing down slightly to gain speed and get out the far side as fast as possible. As the tumult started to die down the port engine rad temperature went off the clock, and my pilot had to feather it. As this engine supplied our heat (as well as powering the H2S), we quickly frosted up inside and couldn't see out. We swung north, came down from 25,000 feet to around 8,000 feet, and took stock. We were without radar, between Berlin and Stettin, flying slowly, and with dawn fast approaching. Calculations showed that as things stood we were unlikely to make England with our stock of petrol and that it would be daylight before we reached the enemy coast. We decided to go to Sweden.

The port engine (which powered the H2S) was unfeathered several times to enable me to get the H2S working and cross the Baltic at a quiet spot. We reached the Swedish coast OK but low cloud prevented us from flying north to Kristianstad where we understood there was a 'drome. We therefore crossed the Swedish coast near Ystad to the accompaniment of a furious shower of Bofors flak, and after much searching for a field big enough to take us, had to land using three fields. This necessitated a 'wheels up' landing and we proceeded to leave bits of Mosquito in two hedges. It was also very noisy. Eventually the farmer arrived and took us to his farm for coffee, saying: 'Welcome to Sweden.'

The local Home Guard also turned up, to take charge of Woollard and his pilot. The accident made only a moderate stir in the local press. News of what was happening on the Mannerheim Line in Finland got the big headline.

A British Mosquito aircraft made a forced landing last night at three o'clock 1 km north-east of Bollerup by the farm belonging to Mr Gustav Hallberg. The aircraft was a complete wreck, but the crew of two escaped unhurt. The Local Defence Volunteers of Valleberga took care of the crew until representatives of the military authorities arrived.

The aircraft arrived here after a raid on Berlin, which was bombed for the third night in a row. The aircraft had taken part in 37 raids on Germany.

'I was outside in the yard a couple of times,' farmer Victor Hilding told the correspondent of *Aurora* on the telephone. Mr Hilding is the nearest neighbour of Mr Hallberg. 'I felt the tension in the air,' he continued, 'and I thought that something was afoot. The aircraft circled many times overhead. Sometimes it came in very low and then climbed away again. It came back and then it happened. With an earsplitting crash it spun around and broke in two in the middle. I was the first man on the spot and I found that the aircraft had come to rest in the refuse pit adjacent to the farmyard. It was smoking a lot but there was no explosion. Seeing the devastation I assumed that the crew lay dead beneath the debris. Soon enough this proved to be wrong, as one of the crew came crawling out. I made it clear to him that he was in Sweden but this he and his comrade were already aware of. We found that the other crew member was sitting jammed among the debris; he was unhurt, though. By this time the military arrived on the spot.'

The two airmen were taken immediately to Ystad where they were quartered in the Hotel Continental. The pilot was the younger, a Scotsman about 20–22 years of age, the other was from London and 30 years of age. The aircraft was totally wrecked. When it tried to make the forced landing its direction of travel was towards the farm of Mr Hallberg, according to the marks in the field. The pilot obviously assumed that the aircraft could land on the 1,000 metre field. But this was not possible, because some hundred metres from the farm there is a deep ditch. On passing this, one of the engines was torn off the aircraft and it is most likely that the aircraft was then out of control. Mr Hallberg thanks providence that the farm escaped undamaged and calls it a miracle that the aircraft did not catch fire, for the wind was blowing towards the farm.

Mr Hallberg regrets that the aircraft passed that part of the sugar-beet field which was thinned out yesterday, as there is a large patch nearby which is not thinned out.

Alan kept a copy of the local paper and had it translated. When eventually his friends read the piece about the Mosquito 'coming to rest in the refuse pit', their inevitable comment was 'Woollard in the s – – t again!'

From Ystad Woollard and his pilot were taken to Malmo; from there they were sent by train to the internment camp at Falun 130 miles north-west of Stockholm, where they remained for more than three months. Sweden had to be most careful of her neutrality, being a small power surrounded by big ones, but by this time it was clear who was going to win the war (a matter of some doubt from 1939 to mid-1944); on 24 September Woollard learned that he was to be repatriated, on the 26th went by train to Stockholm, and on the 28th returned to UK by–Mosquito!

But not in the navigator's seat. British Overseas Airways were running a VIP-passenger and high-value freight service from Sweden, using some Mosquitos because the route ran fairly close to German fighter airfields. Like other passengers, Woollard travelled in some discomfort in the belly of the aircraft. The usual drill was for the passenger to wear full aircrew gear–from flying suit to parachute and oxygen mask–while reclining on a mattress. However, whereas with other aircraft the flight could take up to nine hours, in a Mosquito it was more like three hours. At Bromma airport near Stockholm, it was not unusual to see Lufthansa Ju 52s parked near BOAC machines. They could of course signal home if they saw a British aircraft take off, so there was always the danger of interception by fighters as well as danger of icing. One of the first VIPs to travel in this way by

Mosquito 'airliner' was Niels Bohr, the Danish nuclear scientist, who had escaped from Copenhagen to Sweden and was brought to England on 6 October, 1943. He arrived only half-alive because, his head being too large for him to wear the headphones which were his contact with the pilot, he never heard the order to switch on oxygen, and became unconscious.

Another crew who flew with 139 Squadron from Upwood was Flight Lieutenant Fred Crawley, DFC and Flight Lieutenant Mark Wallis. Crawley tells their story.

The role of our squadron was to act as pathfinders to other Mosquito squadrons, forming a night light bomber force. Our aircraft were mainly Mark 20 Mosquitos, powered by Merlin Packard engines and built in Canada. Radar equipment consisted of 'Gee' and H2S housed in the nose compartment, having a scan of 100 degrees either side of the fore-and-aft line of the aircraft. A normal bomb load would be two 500 lb target indicators, one photo-flash and one 500-lb HE bomb.

In a typical operation 139 Squadron would supply five aircraft to mark the target for the 60–70 'main force' Mosquitos, each of which would be carrying a 4000 lb cookie. The pathfinders would mark each turning point of the route with Verey flares; would broadcast to the main force on VHF the updated winds as the operation progressed; would revise the TOT (Time Over Target) either way, according to the effect of winds different from the flight plan–the duration of the time over the target was normally planned to be two to three minutes only.

Many very good crews did not survive when less able crews did, just because of sheer luck, with mechanical failure and weather being the main features. On our first operation with the squadron, there was a failure of all radar equipment on the run-in to the target. No navigational aids were available for the route home and it was established afterwards that there had been a major change in wind direction from Westward to Northward. To add to the troubles, both Biggin Hill and Woodbridge VHF radio were unable to help. In the event, acting purely on a hunch, a major alteration of course to the North brought us into Southern England and over London, breaking cloud at 2,500 feet–and no balloons were flying that high that night. Sheer luck.

A goodly proportion of pilots and navigators were recruited from those having already completed a tour of operations on heavy bombers. The crews of heavy bombers were a tightly-knit group, but in my experience the bond between the two men in a Mosquito was stronger. Sitting side-by-side in an area not much bigger than a large wardrobe, seeing and sharing everything that was going on, good and bad, was instrumental in bringing this about.

Flying for five hours in the Mosquito was no joke. The 'Gee' and H2S chart were pinned to a small board 18 inches by 12 inches, and navigation was carried out on this balanced on the knees. Lighting was restricted to a single small Anglepoise red lamp with only a pinhole for light emission.

The navigator's seat was a wooden plank with the dinghy on top. Sitting on the dinghy would have been OK–but the valve for inflating it was on top where you sat.

No automatic pilot was fitted and the aircraft had to be flown manually the whole time, causing considerable fatigue.

The pilot's seat was toed-in slightly towards the fore-and-aft line of the aircraft and this sometimes caused the left cheek of the pilot's backside to go to sleep. This in turn gave the impression the aircraft was going over, and it needed firm discipline to believe the instruments. While on conversion to the aircraft, there was a case of a pilot ordering the navigator to bail out because he thought the aircraft was out of control. The navigator was never found.

No toilet facilities existed in the aircraft except for a rubber tube located between the pilot's legs. It was quite a task to use it and the navigator often had to apologise for missing fire.

The programme detailing the names of crews to fly that night on operations usually appeared on the mess notice-board around mid-day. No matter how many operations under one's belt, even the most experienced felt that tightening in the stomach that presaged night operations.

The night-flying test in the afternoon, with its well-tried procedures and familiarity, coupled with the affection that exists between a particular crew and a particular aeroplane, restored the confidence. Later, at the crew briefing, when the target and route details were disclosed, nerves were well under control.

On the night of 9 to 10 December, 1944, the target was Berlin and 139 Squadron were to supply five pathfinders to 64 Mosquitos from main force squadrons. The route was to be: Upwood to the coast and then north eastwards across the North Sea to the redrock island of Heligoland (there was a fighter airstrip on the nearby sand island of Dune)–then landfall north of the wide Elbe estuary–the Great Lakes NW of Berlin–Berlin–return on a straight line to the Zuider Zee and home to base. The bomb load was to be: Target Indicator (Green & Yellow) bursting at 9,800 feet; Target Indicator (Green with Red drip) bursting at 8,000 feet; Photo-flash Red; one 500 lb HE bomb. Weather conditions were described as good for take-off and return at Upwood, with considerable cloud formations over most of Germany.

Upwood at 20.45 hours is a busy airfield, with the Lancasters of 156 Squadron (also operating) and the Mosquitos of 139, vying with one another on the perimeter track, anxious to get airborne.

Rolling now, with a touch of rudder to correct swing, we get off at 20.46 hours and with wheels and flaps up, turn straight away on to the first course of 067, climbing at 160 knots to the English coast at Cromer. The twenty minutes' climb to 17,000 feet at the coast finds the navigator busy using 'Gee' fixes to keep the aircraft on the planned track to the coast. (The calculation of wind speed and direction is not of much use because of the continual increase in height, but the noting of drift often gives indication of what to expect.)

The coastline shows clearly on H2S and Cromer passes underneath at 21.09, when navigation lights and IFF are switched off. The two-stage booster is now put in to the engines and the next 24 minutes has the aircraft climbing to the operational height of 25,000 feet. During this time the navigator fixes the aircraft's position every three minutes by 'Gee' and calculates the wind velocity throughout the height bands. Accurate navigation throughout this stage is vital to the success of the operation, when the aircraft can be flown with no interference from enemy action. On this operation, the calculated winds prove to be considerably stronger than forecast and about 10–15 degrees to the southward of forecast. Navigation proceeds steadily until about 5 degrees east, when enemy jamming of 'Gee' renders the equipment ineffective.

On DR navigation, we turn almost due east running towards Heligoland–a good H2S target and very useful–where the next turning point, about eight miles north of the island, will require a route marker to be fired off for the main force. Although I have never seen an aircraft shot down over the island, their anti-aircraft guns could make it pretty uncomfortable if you strayed too near.

The island of Heligoland appears on the H2S screen and from the present track it is clear we are running too close to the island on the starboard side. An 'S' turn to port puts this right and at 22.02 hours the route marker for the main force is fired to indicate the turning point north of Heligoland. It is bitterly cold, with the outside temperature gauge indicating–50 degrees and the heating system cannot prevent thick ice forming on the inside of the side-blisters.

Approaching the enemy coast, the coastline shows clearly on H2S and once again we have drifted two to three miles south of track of the flight plan. Another route marker is fired crossing the enemy coast with the main force being informed on VHF the marker is three miles south of track. Shortly afterwards two more flares go down on the port side.

At 22.17 radar bearings on Hamburg and Harburg confirm the aircraft is still four miles south of track plan and at 22.25 hours an alteration to port is made to reach the Great Lakes at 22.37 hours.

Here at the Great Lakes the reception committee awaits. The lakes show up so well on radar (despite German attempts to cover them to spoil radar definition), that most operations are routed to the lakes, leaving only a ten-minute run into Berlin. The Germans know this and therefore use the lakes area as a marshalling point for fighters. Usually with a height advantage, and with all the Mosquitos streaming contrails, the night-fighters have a chance to intercept on the run-in to Berlin, when the pathfinder aircraft have to fly straight and level. Heads down and sweat it out, was the order of the day.

On this occasion no night-fighter was seen but heavy ack-ack was predicted as always with remarkable accuracy, and the ride was uncomfortable. The TIs were dropped at 22.45 hours, main force being advised as the drop took place; straight and level for the photograph and then a hard turn to starboard, nose down to reduce height to 22,000 feet and the hard slog home against the wind.

The home trek against a 65-knot headwind meant almost a full hour's flying to reach the enemy coast. 'Gee' was ineffective and pulses would only start to appear through the jamming when approaching the Zuider Zee; the route chosen was well clear of all large towns and H2S gave little or no hope for bearings.

The moon was now well up and the cloud layer well below at around 12–15,000 feet; visibility was good and it was a question of DR navigation and wait for 'Gee' and H2S to come back on line nearing the coast. It is remarkable how lonely it is at 22,000 feet late at night with only the presence of your partner and the occasional brief comment between you to break the loneliness. The aircraft was going well and thoughts of bacon and eggs started to intrude, and yet . . .

About ten degreees east and north of Hanover began the feeling of unease. Nothing appeared to be wrong but the feeling persisted and indeed was getting stronger. A check of fuel, engine gauges, etc., showed nothing out of the ordinary and in desperation I told my pilot I was going to have a look backwards through the astro-dome (the only way you can see aft in a Mosquito).

Unlike daytime when you cannot see easily into

sun, at night you cannot see easily *down* moon as this is the dark side of the sky. Also at night you usually do not see objects you look at directly, so the trick is to keep your head moving and hope to see from the periphery of your eyes. After a good look around and seeing nothing except our own contrails, I was about to sit down when suddenly my eye picked up something on the dark side to starboard. Once having seen something, and just like radar, you can 'wash' it with your eyes and you can see it. And there it was, a single-engined aircraft, slightly down and off to the starboard side, converging slowly.

As the distance between us decreased and with us aware, as the fighter turned towards us we made a steep diving turn to starboard, putting us now in the dark side of the sky. Tracer went over the top of the aircraft but no hits. The westerly course was resumed shortly afterwards and when the feeling of unease returned I needed no telling our friend was back, probably having carried out the same man-oeuvre as ourselves. This time, without waiting for a sighting, a second hard turn to starboard was made, flying on a reciprocal course back into Germany for two minutes before resuming our course homewards. No more unease and I was convinced he had given up.

I have often wondered about this episode. When I do, I always remember how deeply superstitious most aircrew were, always wearing the same things and dressing in the same order, and so on, before an operation; perhaps senses were more finely attuned during those difficult times.

No more problems coming home. The Zuider Zee came up, 'Gee' came back on stream, the gradual let-down over the North Sea to land at base at 01.15 hours. Welcomed by the WAAF Officer in the

debriefing room with hot tea laced with real
Jamaica rum, and bacon and egg in the mess.

Nice to be back.

CHAPTER TWELVE
Berlin
(1944-1945)

In the second half of 1944 the Germans were forced to alter their night defence methods to meet the menace of the Mosquito. For the past year, making use of the fact that burning cities lit up the bombers flying above them, the Germans had introduced the *Wilde Sau* (Wild Boar) system, in which single-seater fighters, faster than the Me 110 and Ju 88, but awkward to handle at night, were allowed free rein, 'roaring about like wild boars', in Luftwaffe jargon.

There were no rules. The Mosquito altered all that, and new tactics and a different organisation involving radio control, sector organisation, and lanes of searchlights, but still using the high-performance single seaters–the Me 109 and the Focke-Wulf 190–was evolved. One of those who successfully used the system was Oberleutnant Fritz Krause, then a staffel-kapitan in 1 Gruppe NJGr 10, who later was promoted to Kommandeur of III Gruppe in NJG 11.

Our main task was to hunt Mosquitos at night at high altitude. In mid-1944 the operational use of the high-performance Mosquito had forced us to reconsider the *Wilde Sau* method of defence. I have a copy (enclosed) of an operation order, which at the time was strictly secret, concerning the new methods of fighting Mosquitos. In particular, there were two different kinds of operation carried out by the Mosquito, which the new system was designed to combat.

The task of testing the new methods was given to the night-hunt experimental station at Berlin Werneuchen. A new two-motor night-hunter suitable to combat the Mosquito, the Heinkel 219, was not quite ready yet, while the jet-hunter, the Me 262, was not available in sufficient numbers. So the task of testing the new methods fell mainly to one staffel of the *Wilde Sau*. We had to meet the two quite different uses of the Mosquito. Firstly, there was the nightly influx of Mosquitos to bomb Berlin; and secondly, there was their use as pathfinders at high altitude across the Ruhr.

Night after night, roughly 30 to 40 Mosquitos flew to Berlin and dropped bombs, and the psychological stress on the Berliners was considerable. Flak and searchlights were moved to Berlin without having any considerable or lasting effect.

The Mosquitos flew at altitudes above 30,000 feet, and after crossing the Elbe lost height so as to be able to fly across Berlin at the highest possible speed in order to avoid the concentrated flak. The direction of the flights across Berlin were different with each operation.

A number of different tactical methods of using night-hunters were tested, but the following method, which I used myself with success, was the most effective. Each time, when the first of the incoming Mosquitos crossed the Rhine, five one-motor hunters took off from Berlin Werneuchen and climbed to their orbiting positions at the height of 35,000 ft. These five waiting positions were each of them marked by a strong master searchlight which lit up in the NE, the NW, the SE, the SW and in the centre of the city of Berlin. It was therefore possible for at least one night-hunter to spot the incoming Mosquitos before they flew across the city, irrespective of the direction from which the attack was coming.

Of course, this depended on good weather and visibility so that the search-lights could pick up the plane at high altitude.

Up to a height of 25,000 feet the flak had their fire-free zone. The area above this limit was reserved for the hunters. The top speed of the one-motor hunter was, in comparison to the Mosquito, in practice, only 60 kph. As there was only a short span of time available for hunting, a considerably greater speed was required to catch them, and this was obtained by making a steep dive from the waiting position. The Mosquitos usually came into Berlin at about 20,000 feet, and the problem now was that the hunters had to avoid the fire of their own flak, because they then frequently entered the area below 20,000 feet. I personally often experienced shells exploding near me, disturbing me while hunting; on one occasion I received a severe hit and was only able to save myself by bailing out with my parachute.

An example of how this special 'anti-Mosquito' method worked is contained in Fritz Krause's action report for 8 July, 1944. He took off from Berlin Werneuchen at 00.40 hours, flying a radar-equipped FW 190 A-5.

I was flying over Berlin when I saw a twin-engined plane caught in the searchlights; it was flying west. I was then at 8,500 metres. I closed in on the plane until I was 700 metres above its level, gave full throttle, and dived. I came too low and opened fire from approximately 200 metres from below and behind at 01.48 and kept firing as I closed. At once, the first shots hit the right motor, an explosion followed, a burst of sparks and then a thick white trail of vapour.

As I had over-shot, I had to stop the attack

momentarily and found myself on the right, alongside the enemy aircraft whose cockade and external fuel tanks I saw clearly, and so was able to identify it without a doubt as a Mosquito.

I fired ESN to draw the attention of the flak and the searchlight to my presence. The enemy 'corkscrewed' in an attempt to evade. Because of the thick 'white flag' of vapour I was able to follow him, although he had already left the searchlight zone in a north-westerly direction.

Following the trail, I managed to attack twice more. At the third attack, I noticed a further explosion on the right wing and an even stronger rain of sparks. At 2,000 metres he disappeared, turning at a flat gliding-angle under my own plane. I did not see the impact on the ground as this was hidden from my angle of view.

On my return flight, passing Lake 'Koppeln', I could estimate the crash-point as 60–70 kilometres north-west of Berlin. When I returned to base a report had already reached them about the crash of a burning enemy aircraft at 01.55 hours at EE-25 to the west of Kürytz. My own plane was covered in oil from the damaged Mosquito. It was called a 'white eleven' and was specially equipped for night-hunting against Mosquitos with Neptun J radar and a long-range fuel-tank. One of the crew of the Mosquito, Flight Lieutenant E. V. Saunders, DFC, bailed out and was taken prisoner. Three days later, at 01.20 hours on 11 July, 1944, I myself had to parachute over Berlin, shot down by Berlin flak!

The high-rise buildings of the German capital restricted the field of fire of any anti-aircraft battery sited at ground level. For this reason three gigantic flak-fortresses had been built. With walls two metres (about six feet) thick, and roofs three metres (more than nine feet) thick, they were impervious to most bombs. There was one such fortress near the Zoo Station, another in Friedrichshain, a kilometre north of the Alexanderplatz, and a third at Humboldt-Hain in the Moabit district. Their height was a minimum 40 metres.

Above each fortress rose two towers. The largest, the Gun Tower, provided a 70 x 70 metres platform for a four-gun battery 12.8 mm pieces, the heaviest available (the standard gun being an 8.8 mm), backed up by the 2 cm *Vierlings-Geschützen*, the four-barrel quads, deadly against low-flying aircraft. The smaller L-Turm provided a platform measuring 15 x 30 metres mounting 3.7 cm flak guns, together with the directional radar and a command post.

Part of the vast space inside the reinforced-concrete fortress was used for troop accommodation, ammunition storage, electricity generators, and so on. In addition, the Zoo fort held a modern Luftwaffe hospital in charge of a doctor personally appointed by Göring, while in the Friedrichshain structure was a smaller hospital and safe-storage rooms for artefacts moved from the museums.

When the air raid sirens sounded, these massive buildings could each give shelter to between 15,000 and 20,000 people. So substantial were they that after the war the Royal Engineers had the greatest difficulty in demolishing one of them.

J. E. L. Gover of 692 Squadron, stationed at Graveley, near Huntingdon, flew 13 operations to Berlin in 1944.

We had to do fifty operations on 692 Squadron, and as you can imagine some were more exciting than others. My most unusual operation was on 14 March, 1944, when the idea was for the Mosquito squadrons to attack Stuttgart after the four-engined heavy bombers had been there. Unfortunately my oxygen equipment was unserviceable and as we used to fly at 28,000 feet, I needed it. It took an hour to

168

transfer the equipment from the reserve aircraft . . . so my navigator and I were all on our own when we got to the target. This normally led to disaster, but luckily for us did not do so on this occasion. There was a sheet of low cloud over the target area, and the heavies had bombed through it, but the heat from the fires that had been started had dissipated the cloud by the time we arrived. We had a grandstand view of two great holes in the cloud through which the fires could be seen burning. This was one of the few occasions on which I felt sorry for the enemy.

Then there was the ill-fated Nuremberg raid on 30 March 1944, which went wrong, resulting in the loss of a large number of aircraft. Nuremberg was out of range for us but we went to Kassel that night in an attempt to fool the enemy into thinking that that was where the main force was going. In this we failed lamentably.

The C-in-C of Bomber Command, Sir Arthur Harris, was, I think, obsessed with attacking Berlin and, I think, rightly so. It was considered, though, that such a target would be out of range, because we carried 600 gallons of petrol which we burned at a rate of 120 gallons an hour, that is, a flying time of five hours. However, if it was possible to send a Mosquito with a 4,000 lb bomb there and back in under five hours, it was far less risky than sending a four-engine heavy bomber, though with more bombs, which would take about eight hours to get there and back.

Therefore it was decided to send us to Berlin with each aircraft carrying a 4,000 lb bomb. On 13 April, 1944 we went there and back in four hours 15 minutes, showing it could be done.

Subsequently, I made twelve further trips to Berlin but never in such a short time. Apart from the second trip on 18 April, when my radar was unserviceable and, far more important, so were my wing tanks carrying a total of 100 gallons of petrol. I just scraped in over the English coast and landed after four hours five minutes' flying time. On the first trip we had more or less gone straight there and straight back, so that it could be done in minimum time, but it would have been a disaster to have kept to the same route on every occasion. Other trips took from four hours 30 minutes to four hours 40 minutes, which left very little spare petrol.

On 4 June, 1944 Gover again took off for Berlin, carrying a 4,000 lb 'cookie'.

As was not uncommon, we were flying west to gain height before turning east. Pressures and temperatures were normal when, at about 5,000 feet and somewhere near Oxford, my port engine stopped without warning. Then it came on again, stopped again, came on again, and then finally stopped.

Normally, with engine failure, one switched off the bad engine and feathered the prop–that is, made it stop completely so as to reduce drag. I did not want to do this, in case it came on again; if I feathered it, it could not possibly have come on again. I was praying devoutly that it would.

The result was, I lost height more quickly than I would if I had feathered it. A Mosquito would fly quite happily on one engine, but not loaded with 600 gallons of petrol and a 4,000 lb bomb.

It was unsafe to jettison a 4,000 lb blast bomb below 4,000 feet. When my engine failed, I was high enough to have done it safely enough for myself, but hardly safely enough for anybody who might be on the ground underneath. I turned east in the hope that I could make the coast and jettison the bomb

170

into the sea.

After a while I saw the lights of a flare path coming up, so I decided to try and do a wheels-up landing; however, I had now lost too much height and, coming in on the approach at 155 mph, hit the ground. There was a half moon which enabled me just to see the ground coming up. I switched off both engines and pulled back on the stick.

The 4,000 lb bomb was very dangerous in that it was all explosive with a very thin casing, and it was liable to go off even if it was not fused. However, it didn't go off. All I remember was a most tremendous jolt, and when I came to I was in a muddy field looking for my helmet—of all things! The aircraft had broken up and caught fire and, although I did not know it at the time, the 4,000 lb bomb had just rolled away.

As a pilot, I had a Sutton harness which consisted of four straps coming up over one's legs and down over one's shoulders. If this equipment was locked, the pilot stayed with the aircraft. I did lock it, although I thought it was useless to do so; in fact it saved my life.

Navigators only had a body belt which meant my poor navigator's head went straight through the instrument panel, and he was killed. This was hardly fair, as he was a married man with two children whereas I was single at the time. As a result of this accident, navigators were provided with Sutton harnesses in the same way as pilots, but it was too late to save poor Ted. I imagine the reason navigators were only provided with body belts before this accident, was because they had to leave their seats to go to the nose of the aircraft to drop the bombs, but they could easily get out of a Sutton harness, so it seems a poor reason.

Of course, there was an enquiry into the accident,

171

but both engines were burnt out, so it was impossible to see what had caused the flow of petrol to stop. Subsequently, the same thing happened to somebody else on another squadron, but he jettisoned his bomb too low and blew himself up. The next time the same thing happened, it was to somebody in my own squadron, but he was only testing his aircraft by day with no bomb aboard. The result was that he made a successful single-engine landing, the fault was found and put right; and we had no further trouble.

I had suffered second degree burns and had to go to hospital and it wasn't until 10 August, 1944 that I went back on operations. No prizes for guessing the target–Berlin!

Gover's arrival over Stuttgart alone, on the heels of a main force raid, was accidental; and Gover was fortunate. Not so Flight Lieutenant L. F. King, a pathfinder pilot of 105 Squadron, in Bennett's 8 Group, who was sent out alone in a Mark 16 Mosquito carrying a 4,000 lb bomb to Wetter in the Ruhr, timed to arrive when the raid was over, the defences fully alerted and able to concentrate on a single raider. His widow, Mrs Kay M. King, was never told why he–a pathfinder normally carrying flares–was sent out in a bomber version of the Mosquito and, dangerously, at the tail end of a thousand-bomber raid.

I was surprised, because he had just gone back to RAF Bourn off leave, and rung up and told me that he wasn't going out that night. It was an awful night, the wind howling, windows rattling, raining, and I was thinking: Thank goodness, Len isn't out tonight. Then, in the afternoon–it was 19 March, 1945–I received the telegram. *Missing.*

We married in 1940 when he was already in the

RAF, but we had known each other when we were children. He was on Spitfires then, with 64 Squadron at Kenley. Later, he became an instructor in blind flying–beam approach on Oxfords. Many of his pupils went on to Mosquitos and became pathfinders. One Wing Commander said to him: 'You're delivering new pilots to us, but what we want is *you*.' This was because of his experience of instrument flying. He converted to Mossie IIIs in December 1944, and by February 1945 was flying Mark IVs. The Mosquito was an aircraft you had to fly, he said, whereas the Oxford flew itself. When he was at Kenley we lived near the aerodrome, but when he went to an operational Mosquito squadron we discussed it and decided that he must concentrate on his job, so I went to stay with friends. He went back after that leave, was warned for an op and then it was cancelled. After the telegram, I left it a week and then went and saw his CO. I learned that my husband had been wakened at 4 a.m. to fly to Wetter with a 4,000 lb bomb just after a raid by 1,000 bombers, but no one could explain why. The CO thought he might very well turn up, as there was such chaos in Germany then.

Flight Lieutenant King's logbook shows that on 18 March he did a local flight in a Mark XVI (the Mosquito modified to take the 4,000 pounder), presumably an air test before that night's op. The last entry read: DEATH PRESUMED.

King had joined on a Short Service commission for six active years, with a £100-a-year gratuity payable at the end of that time, so that he could set himself up in civilian life. None of the gratuity was payable to his widow, as her husband, having done only five and three-quarters years, had 'failed to fulfil his contract'.

But it was the 'complete mystery' concerning that last

operation which worried Mrs King. Another pathfinder suggested to her that as it was a particularly foul night, he could have flown into a towering cumulus cloud which could have broken the Mosquito. The only real clue she got was that his aircraft was fitted with Oboe and that for some operations there was a requirement for the Mosquito to be flown straight and level for 10 minutes, which made it a good target for flak.

According to Fritz Krause, the German night-fighters called this navigational technique the 'boomerang' method. To counteract it, they employed a scheme similar to the one they used for the protection of Berlin, which had caused the Mosquito bombings to become more scattered.

Due to the tremendous performance of the Mosquito, this plane could be operated over the Ruhr area at 33,500 feet and could therefore be guided very exactly by air control centres in England. By this method the accurate dropping of bombs, and, what was even more dangerous, the brightly shining marker flares which served as targets for the bomber units following the Mosquitos, was made possible. All important targets in the Ruhr area, particularly the Hydrierwerke, Wesseling and Knapsack, were particularly vulnerable.

The weak point of this British pathfinder technique was the technical requirement to hold a north-south or south-north course at approximately 33,500 feet for five to ten minutes. We had some success against them, but nevertheless the pilots of the night-hunters thought our efforts pointless, just a waste of time.

Flight Lieutenant George Nunn, who served for a time with 105 Squadron flying the Mosquito XVIs equipped with Oboe, described the method from the RAF point of view.

Oboe was a bombing technique and very clever. There were two radar transmitting stations in England, measuring distances. You flew to a collecting point and from there single aircraft, one at a time, made ten-minute runs to the target. You flew at a given height and at a given speed. Signals were sent to you–dots or dashes–to correct you left or right. The pilot had to concentrate on the flying (you were covered in perspiration at the end of the ten minutes), while the navigator got the signals telling him when to bomb. We were being watched by the radar and the radar was measuring the distances. That's why we could use only one aircraft at a time. The Germans never found out how it worked, but they knew the aircraft had to fly at the same height and speed for ten minutes, So this was where the fighters might latch on to you.

George Nunn had begun his career as a soldier in the pre-war Territorial Army. He was called up in August, 1939, and sent to an interview board for possible officer training. When asked what unit he would like (and the Colonel by that meant tanks, guns, or regiment), Nunn's reply was: RAF. The Colonel went purple. However, he was sent a form to fill in and began pilot training in 1941. He graduated on Wellingtons, his first operation being the 1000-bomber raid on Cologne in May 1942, and after that Essen, 'a shambles as far as we were concerned'. A tour in the Middle East followed, extended for the turning-point battle of El Alamein. While being flown back to Britain in a Halifax, it lost two engines over the desert and they all had to bail out. Found by, fortunately, friendly Arabs, they reached Gibraltar and from there got back home with the Navy. A spell as an instructor on Wellingtons with an operational training unit followed. After being accepted for Mosquitos, Nunn was posted to 608 Squadron, which flew Candadian-built Mark 25s, and was on ops virtually every night.

We only had two stand-downs in a month. Of 25 or
26 ops done by the Squadron, 18 were on the Berlin
run with four 500 lb bombs. I then converted to the
mark XVI with the 4,000 pounder and stayed with
them to the end of the war. The Mosquito was an
incredibly good aeroplane, particularly the Mark
XVI. I came back on one engine several times, after
being hit by shrapnel. 8 Group (PFF) bombed
Berlin almost every night for a month with about
100 Mosquitos, which must have added up in terms
of bomb-load; with very low losses. We always
bombed on markers laid by other Mosquitos; sometimes there were route-markers as well as sky-
markers and ground-markers. They routed us so we
didn't do the same thing twice, and over a number
of towns to make them all have a false alert. To
Berlin and back usually took between four hours 10
minutes and four hours 20 minutes. Fast! One night
we had a route straight to Berlin and back. Three
hours 40 minutes to back over base; and another 10
minutes in the queue to land. Sometimes we sent off
one aircraft every hour to some poor town in
Germany, to affect morale.

The Mosquito was a lovely aeroplane, but a lot of
people didn't like it. It tended to swing on take-off
and landing, although I wasn't bothered by the high
landing speed. But big people did find it a bit
crowded, particularly the navigator. There was a
proper pilot's seat, but the navigator sat slightly
behind on a bench, and had to lamber down into
the nose to do the bombing. He had a chest-type
parachute, but the pilot had a lot of junk hanging
on to him–he sat on his parachute, with the dinghy
attached. It would have been hard for the pilot to
get out if the navigator was dead. I lost touch with

176

my navigator on demob in November 1945, but met
him again in October 1986.

The night over Berlin which they both vividly remembered was 14 April, 1945. 608 Squadron, as part of
Bennett's pathfinding 8 Group, was stationed at Downham Market near Kings Lynn. George Nunn and his
navigator, H. S. T. Harris, DFC, then a Pilot Officer, had
flown their particular Mosquito 6T-U for a total of 11
hours before take-off at 11.09 p.m. Harry Harris tells this
part of the story.

It was a warm spring night and the aircraft was
reluctant to leave the ground as, apart from a full
load of fuel, it carried a 'cookie', a large cylindrical
drum containing 4,000 lbs of high explosive. A
minute later the aircraft staggered into the air and
started the long, slow climb to 27,000 feet.
  As the roof of the crew compartment was perspex
the view from both seats was very good. In addition
there was a perspex 'blister' on the side of the
canopy next to the navigator. By putting his head in
the 'blister' he could see to the rear of the aircraft.
The ability to see behind us was to play a vital part
in just over two hours' time.
  The route was via Clacton which was reached at
11.34 p.m. Our height was then 17,000 feet. From
there we crossed the sea to reach the enemy coast
at Westkapelle at 11.54 p.m. At 11.59 the heading
was changed to fly directly to Berlin. At 12.07 a.m.
cruising level at 27,000 feet was reached and we
settled down to another hour's run to the target.
  It was black all around, although the stars shone
brightly above. The navigational aid 'Gee' was
working well and fixes were obtained until 12.57.
The route had taken us north of the Ruhr and then
between Hanover and Magdeburg, avoiding the

heavily-defended areas of Germany. As we cruised at 310 mph we had no fear of enemy fighters as only jets could get at us and we thought they were few and far between. And they would not bother us when the heavy four-engined bombers were attacking other targets that night, including Magdeburg. We passed 10 miles north of it at 1 a.m.

Although we knew there were Mosquitos all around us heading for Berlin we saw none. On a previous trip one had crossed only about 30 feet above us, the flames from his exhausts terrifyingly close.

George had previously done a tour of operations in Wellington bombers in North Africa and I had completed a tour on Lancasters over Germany. We were no strangers to flak or fighters but there was always some apprehension as the target was approached. Mine came mainly from the thought that I might have made an error in navigation and that at the appointed time there would be no sign of the Target Indicators (TIs) going down on the target. These TIs were placed over the target by the Pathfinder Force and tonight they would illuminate at 01.11, 01.12, 01.13 and 01.14 a.m. Green-coloured markers at 5,000 feet, red at 7,000 feet and yellow at 10,000 feet. The lower the markers the more accurate they ought to be.

In the event the first TIs did not show until 01.16. At that time I was down in the nose ready to bomb. As we spotted the TIs a blue beam flashed across the sky and stayed on our aircraft. This was a master searchlight, controlled by radar, and deadly accurate in picking out its victim. Within seconds ten or twelve white searchlight beams lit up our aircraft. For us this was not unusual. Nearly every time we went to Berlin we got coned. The good thing about it was that when I was down in the bombing position

I didn't have to fumble around with a torch to set up the bombing instruments. With searchlights it was clearer than day. But that night they came too late to help me, as the bombing run had started. As the searchlights were positioned on the outer areas of Berlin they in no way affected the bombing run. At 01.18 I pressed the bomb release and the 'cookie' slipped gently off the bomb-rack and sped on its destructive way. The aircraft had to be flown straight and level for the next 42 seconds. This was the moment the cookie should reach the ground and explode, the aerial camera mounted in the aircraft hopefully photographing the point of impact. At 01.19 another group of TIs burst over the target, but by that time the cookie had exploded.

George Nunn confessed to having something of a reputation for being caught in searchlights, but in fact this seems to have been the result of the Luftwaffe's new anti-Mosquito methods. On this occasion, he recalled:

The heavies were doing their stuff on Potsdam, just outside Berlin. It was fairly spectacular, they seemed to have set fire to everything around. We were caught in the searchlights, having bombed on the markers and turned for home. The area illuminated by searchlights was too big to get out of, it was just a big pool of light made by perhaps 15 searchlights, with you in the middle. No violent weaving, because that just kept you longer in the cone. Best to get out of the area as fast as you can. The nav was watching behind us, and I heard him call: 'Fighter!'

Harry Harris recollected the same sequence of events, but more of the dialogue.

We made a turn to the left, climbing steadily, until we were heading westwards for home. We did not even try tc get out of the searchlight cone as it would be quite impossible. The flak was below us and then it stopped. As we settled on course for home at 01.25 the searchlights suddenly went out.

I looked through the 'blister' to the rear of the aircraft and saw we were making extremely thick condensation trails. These are commonly seen today in the wake of high-flying jets and are caused by the heat from the engines condensing the water or ice crystals in the air into clouds, very white clouds, streaming out behind the aircraft. As I looked behind I saw a red and a green light just above our contrail. I said to George: 'Some idiot is flying with his navigation lights on and is following behind us.'

As I said this I realised the lights were gaining on us very fast. I then knew it was not one of ours but the dreaded German jet. At that moment a white light appeared between the red and green lights from the nose of the aircraft. As it did I shouted:

'Dive to starboard–Go!'

Simultaneously three things happened. The searchlights from the ground came on, bathing our aircraft in dazzling light. Secondly, George flung the Mosquito over to the right, pushing its nose hard down. And thirdly, a hail of coloured lights came across the top of the canopy. The fighter was firing and had just missed the cockpit, the cannon shells and tracer bullets missing us by inches. George said a rude word and pulled the aircraft over to the left.

The change of attitude must have been sufficient for the light cone to flood the cockpit. George Nunn recalled the result.

I got slightly blinded. The next thing I knew we were

180

upside down. The nav was not strapped in, because he had been down in the nose, bombing. So, at that moment, he was up against the roof, all the gyros had toppled and so the instruments went beserk.

Harris's situation was perhaps even more confusing than the plight of his pilot.

As the aircraft was pushed around by George, I lost all sense of direction or attitude. I was forcibly shot out of my seat, and crashed into the top of the perspex canopy. Then I was floating in the cockpit. Also floating was my parachute, which I grabbed and clipped on to my parachute harness. This harness was worn before entering the aircraft and the parachute itself was stowed in a special container in the bomb-aimer's position. The violent movements of the aircraft had dislodged it. It has two 'D' rings which clip onto two hooks on the harness, and the parachute was then in place on the chest–ready to jump.

As I clipped on the parachute George said, very quietly: 'I can't see. I've been blinded by the searchlights. Bail out, quickly.'

Having assured me that he would follow me out, I scrambled down to the nose, where the escape hatch was situated. It consisted of a square hole in the floor, with a door on the inside floor and another on the other side. This was the normal method of entry and exit. I found the handle, but I could not budge the door. Suddenly it was pitch black. The searchlight had gone out.

I cursed then, as I could not see and I could not open the escape hatch, possibly due to the twisting action of the aircraft or due to pressurisation. I gave it up and went back to George. He was still in his seat.

As the aircraft turned over slowly, I saw fire

through the top of the cockpit. I was looking down at the ground, and the fires were the result of the heavy bomber attack on Potsdam.

I asked George if he could see. He had closed his eyes to try to get his vision back. As several minutes had passed since he was blinded, I asked him if he would open his eyes and look for the fires. Fortune was with us as he saw the red light of the fires, now on his left side. Using the fires as reference, he slowly and carefully brought the aircraft on to a level keel. The instruments on the flight panel were useless. All the gyro-operated ones were spinning furiously, including the artificial horizon and compass.

A careful reading of the altimeter, still moving erratically, showed the height as 20,000 feet. Then, checking even more carefully, we found it to be 2,000 feet–only 1,600 feet above the ground. A check on my watch showed it was 15 minutes since evasive action had started. The Mosquito had descended at about 2,000 feet per minute, so, luckily for us, it must have stayed level or even gained height at times.

Using burning Potsdam as a datum, I was able to give George a direction to go for England, and then we climbed hurriedly away, shaken but undismayed. As the gyros settled we were able to resume normal flight and 110 minutes later were over base.

An inspection of the aircraft on the ground showed a hole through the rudder and through the tail fin where a cannon shell had been. Following this line of sight, it missed the cockpit by an estimated three inches. There was no trace of any other hits.

While on the staff of the RAF Flying College in 1955 I read a report by a German pilot of an Me 262. On 15 April 1945 he shot down a Mosquito just north of Berlin at 01.30 hours. Apparently he couldn't follow us down!

George Nunn commented: 'I flew back on the Turn & Bank Indicator until the instruments recovered. We were minus half the tail, but this didn't affect the flying qualities of the aircraft.'

Wing Commander 'Dickie' Blyth, DSO, DFC, told David King (of De Havilland's) about an extraordinary encounter he had over Berlin at about this time, the spring of 1945. He was cruising homewards after photographing the results of the raid when, with no warning, an aircraft with twin nacelles but no propellors, and complete Luftwaffe insignia, came up very quickly behind him. As he applied full boost to his Mosquito, the German aircraft took up station beside him without the least difficulty, then pulled ahead, turned across his bows, completed the circle and came up on his tail. He and his observer waited for the bang, but after circling him twice more, it disappeared. He had of course heard stories about enemy jets and it was his good fortune that his first and only encounter was with an unarmed Arado or Me 262.

By now, the war in Europe was almost over. There had been a slight delay in launching the final offensive across the Rhine, because of Hitler's ill-advised and ill-fated gamble in the Ardennes just before Christmas, 1944. Derek Bovet-White, who had been attacking V-1 sites in daylight in the spring of that year, now found himself flying support to the Americans from 18 December to 31 January, often in weather so foul that the 'Gee'-equipped Mosquitos were often the only aircraft aloft, fore-runners of today's all-weather fighters.

In order to attack in the west, Hitler had had to weaken his already hard-pressed forces on the eastern front, and on 12 January, 1945 the last Russian offensive began. This was to prove one factor among many in launching multiple air attacks by the RAF and USAAF on Dresden, beginning on the night of 13 February. The first wave of attack by RAF Bomber Command was led by Mosquitos of 5 Group. After the area had been illuminated by four-engined pathfinders, eight Mosquitos of 627 Squadron marked the aiming point at low level, using the method pioneered by Cheshire, and controlled by a Master Bomber, Wing Commander Maurice A. Smith, DFC, also flying a Mosquito at low level. There was little flak and the night-fighters were ineffective; the attack went perfectly. But it was the heavier second wave of attack which touched off the firestorm that made Dresden a name to rank with that of Hiroshima later.* The effect on the war, however, was negligible. The decisive blows were being struck by the armies. Germany was being over-run from East and West simultaneously. Flight Lieutenant Fred Crawley, DFC, who, with his navigator Flight Lieutenant Mark Wallis, had made a number of memorable trips to Berlin in 1944, was also there to see the end in 1945.

During the last few months of the war, the Mosquito night-bomber force was assigned almost entirely to Berlin. During these operations in April 1945, the progress by the Russian forces from the east was very plain and on 19 April the squadron carried out what proved to be the last operation against the city. On this occasion, tracer from field artillery could be seen going into Berlin itself. About this time the puppet government of Germany was set up in Kiel.

For many aircrew, there now began to intrude the nagging thought that with the war nearly over, there was a good chance of surviving and sleeping regularly in bed at nights. But at the same time, the devil's

---

* The part played by the Mosquitos at the head of the first wave is described fully in the author's *Dresden 1945: The Devil's Tinderbox* (Souvenir Press, 1982).

tail was lashing away. . . wouldn't it be b - - - - y awful to get the chop (for any reason) during the last few days of hostilities.

Operations were resumed on 22 April and again on the 23rd with the target on both occasions being Kiel, only Mosquito aircraft being involved. The opposition was negligible. Then followed a long break in operational flying until, somewhat with surprise, crews were briefed on 2 May for another visit to Kiel. This operation was to prove to be the last operation of the war against Germany.

By now, the main topic in the mess was when hostilities would cease, with an avid interest in the charts and maps showing the Allied advances on the various fronts. The night-flying test during the afternoon of 2 May was carried out with meticulous care to ensure everything was on top line; many things besides enemy action could bring about the loss of an aircraft and crew, and no one wanted to bow out at the winning line.

The scene set up was, therefore, an operation of just over three hours flying to what would normally be considered a relatively easy target, with no weather problems. As a backcloth, the ever-intruding thought that this could be the last one of the war.

The route to Kiel presented no problems, with radar being subject to less jamming, but the approach to the target was very different. It was eerie–no searchlights, no flak, no nothing. One felt like talking in whispers so as not to distort the unnatural quiet, the quiet of the graveyard, and as the target indicators were called down, even this was done in a quieter voice than usual.

As the turn for home was made, a fleeting thought for the vanquished, but a growing warm tide of excitement at the prospect of survival.

After the cessation of hostilities in May 1945,

flights were authorised to allow aircrew and ground staff who wished to go, to see areas of Western Germany that had been subjected to major air attack from night operations.

What could be seen in the Ruhr (the Happy Valley of so many costly operations) was beyond wildest expectations. Towns like Cologne, Duisburg, Essen, Dusseldorf, seemed to have been crushed into gigantic heaps with cleared ribbons of roads running through them. No signs of life, no activity and seemingly the destruction going on and on and on.

There was little talking in Lancaster 'Z' Zebra as it flew steadily down the Ruhr valley eastwards. The ground staff standing in the crew area up front beginning to appreciate the awesome power they had nurtured and prepared; the aircrew remembering what it was like to deliver and remembering also good friends who had paid the ultimate price.

CHAPTER THIRTEEN
Shipping Strike (1943-1945)

There were three main types of shipping target for the Strike Wings of Coastal Command, which operated closely with the Navy. There was the traffic between Norway and Germany, which included the iron-ore essential to the German war economy and also supplies for the Wehrmacht garrisons in Norway. A much tougher target consisted of the German capital ships which used the northern fjords as ambush bases for forays into the Atlantic or against the Allied convoys to Russia. Then, down in the Bay of Biscay and the western entrance to the English Channel lay the routes for U-boats leaving from or returning to their French bases, often on the surface.

307 (City of Lwów) Squadron had been formed from Polish airmen who had escaped to Britain, and, like all Polish units, had a formidable reputation. They were early equipped with the Mosquito. On 13 June, 1943 a detachment from this squadron which was stationed at Predannack in Cornwall for anti-shipping patrols, known as 'Insteps', took off on its first operation of this type. Bad weather led to an early return. The following day, however, was quite different, as the squadron's Operations Record Book testifies.

Weather fair to cloudy. The second Instep patrol was flown this day and provided a measure of excitement. The formation of four Mosquitos consisted of three from this squadron, S. Ldr. Szablowski (Pilot) and Sgt. Gajewski (Nav. Radio),

F.O. Pelka (Pilot) and F/Sgt. Zakrocki (Nav. Radio), and F. O. Gorzanka (Pilot) and F. O. Maluszek (Nav. Radio) in company with F. O. Harris (Pilot) and Sgt. Skeel of 410 Squadron (R.C.A.F.) At 09.30 hours at 44° 50′ N. 08°50 W, the formation led by S. Ldr. Szablowski saw five U-Boats on the surface. The leader ordered line astern and directed the attack against the second U-Boat, he saw strikes on the conning tower; he then attacked the third submarine, again seeing strikes. The submarines set up a heavy barrage from quick firing guns and L.M.Gs.S. Ldr Szablowski's port engine was hit and stopped. F. O. Pelka, coming in second, found his cannon would not fire. The third and fourth aircraft did not attack because by then the barrage had really got going and because S. Ldr. Szablowski's engine was smoking. The engagement was broken off and S. Ldr. Szablowski returned on one engine (a distance of some 500 miles) and made a belly landing at Predannack (Hydraulics worked by port engine). The remainder completed their patrol. Weather at place of attack 3 to 5/10s at 1500 visibility 10 to 15 miles, some precipitation.

Five days later, another Instep patrol led by Squadron Leader Szablowski found a more vulnerable target than submarines, with their thick pressure-hulls and heavy flak armament. Flying with him were the Mosquitos of Flying Officer Pelka and Flight Lieutenant Bienkowski, together with a Canadian Mosquito from 410 Squadron flown by Flying Officer Murray. They sighted a Blohm und Voss 138 three-engined, twin-fuselaged reconnaissance flying boat, low down over the sea.

S Ldr. Szablowski ordered the formation into line astern and swung in to attack. F. O. Murray did not understand the order and came in sharply to attack independently. His turn was too sharp and his first attack was ineffective. The other three aircraft attacked in turn and all saw strikes. The Bv 138 climbed for cloud but S. Ldr Szablowski and F. O. Pelka were able to get in a second attack from head-on. The enemy aircraft was smoking but still appeared able to climb, so S. Ldr. Szablowski went above it and ordered F. O. Pelka to remain below. The enemy aircraft just reached the cloud base and staggered; F. O. Pelka delivered the *coup de grace*; the e/a crashed into the sea and caught fire. Three survivors were seen to reach a dinghy.

The Blohm und Voss normally carried a crew of six and were armed with 20 mm cannon in two turrets, plus one machine-gun.

Cornwall was fine for operations flown over the Bay of Biscay, but the airfield chosen as a base for the harassing of Norwegian waters was at almost the other end of the British Isles–Banff, near the Moray Firth, almost opposite Stavanger in Southern Norway. Bill Clayton-Graham, DFC, recalled:

BanffStrike Wing was formed in September, 1944 when Mosquitos of 235 and 248 Squadrons were transferred from Portreath in Cornwall, joining up with 333 Squadron crewed by Norwegians. Occasionally they combined operations with Beaufighter squadrons based at Dallachy–not over-popular with the Mosquito pilots who had to throttle back to a cruising speed of 180 knots for the Beaufighters instead of our normal cruising speed of 220 knots. In November 143 Squadron, newly-equipped with Mosquitos, joined the Banff Wing.

I joined 235 Squadron on 1 November, 1944 for my third tour of operations, my first strike being made on 8 November.

Our armament was four machine-guns and four 20 mm cannon and with the ability to carry bombs. 248 Squadron had some aircraft equipped with the 'Tsetse' gun, replacing the cannons and firing a 57-mm 6 lb shell. It retained its four machine-guns.

Our Mosquitos were not equipped with Rocket Projectiles (RPs) until early 1945, first used on operations in February. The eight RPs (four under each wing) were normally armed with 25-lb armour-piercing warheads, but occasionally these were replaced with 60-lb semi-armour-piercing HE warheads.

A 50 or 100 gallon drop-tank was fitted under each wing for longer flights, and with four RPs also under each wing, they tended to wag a bit at take-off!

Normally, when making an attack on shipping, the dive at approximately 45° was started at 2,000 feet, opening up with machine-guns as sighters at about 1,500 to 1,000 feet, then the cannons hopefully to knock out the ship's guns, bridge, etc., and firing the RPs at about 500 feet. These were set to form a pattern spread on impact, so that if aimed correctly about half hit the target above the waterline, the other four undershooting slightly to hit below the waterline.

Some rockets would pass right through the ship, others would enter and ricochet around inside like a demented hornet, wreaking havoc internally and generally starting a fire.

The main danger in this sort of attack, apart from the obvious, such as enemy fire, was the possibility of flying into your target. Being in a dive, with a closing speed of around 300 mph, you have to pull out very smartly. On one occasion Flight Lieutenant Gerry Yeates had a close shave. As he pulled out, he hit the masthead of the ship. On landing back at

Banff, the top of the mast, complete with German flag, was found embedded under the aircraft's nose!

Some aircraft had a ciné camera mounted in the nose just above the machine-guns, recording when either set of guns was fired. If your aircraft did not have a ciné camera, the navigator was issued with a hand-held F24 camera.

A series of attack photographs illustrate Bill Clayton-Graham's recollections, based on his log. The first series was taken on 26 December, 1944, backed up by photos taken from an accompanying aircraft of Clayton-Graham limping home on one engine.

The five photographs taken by my excellent navigator, Flying Officer 'Ginger' Webster, are of an attack on two merchant ships in Leirvik harbour using machine-guns and 20 mm cannon. The last two shots show me firing on the nearest ship, after which I went on to attack the second ship, when I was hit in the port engine. One ship was left sinking, the other on fire. Our strike force totalled twelve aircraft.

As I broke off the second attack, smoke was pouring from my port engine, which I feathered, and I flew round the headland (on right of picture) to go down the fjord and out to sea, having climbed to 1,000 feet.

Heavy flak burst around me in the fjord, and then I saw fighters in line astern flying with me about 1,000 feet above and slightly astern to my right– about 24 of them. As they peeled off to attack I turned into them and attacked with machine-guns (my cannon were spent), which forced about 12 of them (Me 109s and FW 190s) to dive past my nose and through my line of fire. I saw one hit well and truly, and I must have tickled quite a few others.

I was not hit but was a sitting duck with only one engine. I turned back on course out to sea, dived onto the wave-tops with the good engine at full throttle and awaited the second attack, which never came. They had all gone on to attack another aircraft flown by my good friend, F/O Jim Fletcher, whom they shot down. One enemy fighter was reported by the Norwegian underground to have been shot down.

Our strike leader, Squadron Leader 'Jacko' Jackson-Smith, who had seen my predicament but had lost sight of me, called me up and told me to fire a Verey light so he could come and escort me. I replied:

'Not b - - - - y likely, they'll see me, too!'–and pressed on.

About 20 miles out to sea, I called up the patrolling Air-Sea Rescue Warwick, which carried a lifeboat. He homed in on me (I was doing about 170 mph) and escorted me back the 300-odd miles over the North Sea to Banff. Two photographs of my Mossie were taken from this Warwick on the way home.

The Mossie handled beautifully and I made a safe wheels-down landing. A piece of shrapnel was found, which had cut a coolant pipe in my port engine.

A change of underpants and several pints of beer were the only 'repairs' needed by me.

On 9 January, 1945 Clayton-Graham was with a force of 18 Mosquitos which attacked eight merchant ships in Leirvik harbour with cannons and machine-guns. Only one, rather damaged photograph, illustrates this.

We left three ships on fire. The Norwegian underground later reported one ship sunk at its moorings and four others severely damaged; also that the ship in the photograph had unloaded ammunition which was stacked alongside the quay. Happily this did not go up during our attack. We had a fighter escort of 12 Mustangs, but they were not needed on this occasion.

Despite fighter cover from either Mustangs or Mosquitos, German fighters had some successes, the worse that I can recall being on 15 January, 1945. Fourteen strike Mosquitos plus two Norwegian Mosquito outriders were jumped by nine FW 190s. We had no fighter cover and six Mosquitos were shot down, plus one FW 190. However, two large merchant ships and an escort vessel were sunk.

This strike was led by Maurice Guedj, popularly known as 'Maury', who was the most decorated Free French pilot, having a Paris street named after him. He was now CO of 143 Squadron. Wallace Woodcock had known him since their first tour on Beaufighters, when, as a humble Pilot Officer, Maurice led a walk-out of all the aircrews from the 'Officers Only' bar near their airfield. As a 'sprog' Sergeant Pilot, Woodcock appreciated that.

'Maury', Norman Smith of Toronto, and I were the first three pilots to survive a complete tour on long-range day Beaufighters with 248 Squadron. Maury got back on ops by threatening to resign his commission and join the Free French commandos. Every month for thirteen months, he and I applied for me to rejoin him in 248 Squadron, now equipped with Mossies. He was then 'B' Flight commander, but I elected to join 'C' Flight with Mark XVIIIs (Tsetses), as my old friend Johnny Hayton was on that flight.

Few of the big-gun Mosquitos were ever made, and 'C'

Flight of 248 were the only flight equipped with them.

The best thing I can say for the Tsetse is that it provided a different and confusing direction of attack for the defending gunners. Attacking in a Mark VIII required a dive from approximately 5,000 feet at a 30° angle with the turn-and-bank indicator dead central. The slightest drift would cause the gun to jam. Our aim was to put armour-piercing shells (3,000 feet per second muzzle-velocity) through the deck planking of the ships while the rocket went in at 500 feet in a shallow dive. Occasionally, when a Tsetse wasn't available, I borrowed a Mark VI. It was so different, I almost forgot to take the rocket 'safety' off on one attack! Another disadvantage of the Tsetse was its shorter range compared to the Mark VI.

On 15th January, 1945, Maury was now commanding 143 Squadron as its previous CO had 'bought it' a week or so previously. Sixteen of us took off for Leirvik (about 70 miles up the Sogne fjord), but I was the only one in a Mark XVIII carrying the six-pounder gun. We virtually caught them with their pants down. Only Sergeant Clew got hit (in one engine), and as he couldn't make it over the mountains, he flew down the fjord accompanied by Maury, Freddy Alexandre (a Philadelphian) and others. The rest of us circled at the entrance; but as they arrived we were jumped by about 30 FW 190s. We lost five out of 16 that day, but of all my friends who 'got the chop' I think that Maury got to me the most.

The Strike Wing was led by the one-and-only Group Captain Max Aitken (son of Lord Beaver-brook). What a man! The story goes that when informed by Group that 'station commanders do NOT fly on operations', he sent a terse, two-word message back, the second being '- - - - you!' I could go on about the fun we had flying for Max Aitken– what a gang! Every other station commander would lecture you what would happen if you were caught low flying. He said, do all you like but let us know; I will cover for you. And the party he gave to all the fishing fleet skippers when one of 333 Squadron's boys clipped the mast of a trawler. 333, they were something.

Notwithstanding Flying Officer Woodcock's reservations about the six-pounder gun, his log shows that he did some damage with it. On 28 September, 1944, while on anti-U-Boat patrol off Sondersund, he attacked a torpedo-boat, scored nine hits with the Tsetse, and saw it sink–in spite of 'accurate hate from Christiansand'. He scored hits on quite a number of naval targets in October, and then, on 29 November, while on anti-U-boat patrol off Lista, he saw a U-boat. He dived and fired eight six-pounder rounds at it, scoring two hits.

This at the time was supposedly the nearest a Mossie had got to sinking one. I did hear a rumour that Halifaxes got it later when it had to surface, but this was never confirmed.

I was fairly lucky in most of my strikes. However, there was a problem sometimes for us, because we had to leave the formation when near the target to climb to 5,000 feet, while the others stayed low. For instance, on 7 December, 1944, a formation of about 90 aircraft (the entire Banff Mossie Wing, plus the Beaufighter Wing from Dallachy) was sent to prang a large convoy holed up in Aalesund Harbour. We had a very ambitious leader, but even I, a mere pilot, could see our landfall was spot on target; nevertheless he turned north and led us up the coast for about 60 miles until we were near a

Luftwaffe airfield, when we were jumped'. The four Mark XVIIIs, flying at 5,000 feet above the rest, were jumped first.

Bill Cosman and K. C. Wing (both Canadians) and Brian Beathe (a South African) went down. I was able to chase an Me 109 off Brian's tail, then I went down and strafed the airfield, but was jumped later. However, I made it back to Sumburgh in the Shetlands (I think I was still taking evasive action, even then!). Bill and K. C. didn't make it. In the Ops Room at Sumburgh the leader was claiming we were jumped at Aalesund. We soon disillusioned him on that point!

In 1948, while rehashing the mission in the Bermuda War Veterans Club, a 404 Squadron Beaufighter pilot, Hugh Watlington, told me that he saw it all–that as I peeled off to protect Brian, *two* Me 109s screwed up their attack on me! Till then, I never knew. The losses were horrendous–30, I think–and all for nothing.

The short range of the Tsetses, compared with the Mark VIs, caused us to be detached from Banff to North Coates in Lincolnshire to operate with Dave Cartridge's Torbeau squadron in the dying days of the war when I was 'C' Flight's last commander.

Clayton-Graham of 235 Squadron had contrasted memories, happy and unhappy. A lark with an improvised sledge towed round the snow-bound airfield by a Hillman van, everyone falling off outside the HQ block at the feet of Group Captain Aitken and an Air Commodore, and as they scrambled to their feet, picked up their caps, and saluted, Aitken saying: 'Survival training, sir–carry on, chaps!'

'The fishermen of MacDuff. If they were out at sea when we took off on a strike they remained there

196

until we returned, sometimes up to six hours, in case someone had to ditch. We used to drink with them in their local pub–and could they drink!–and one night I and two others were invited aboard a trawler for a 'last drink' around 11 p.m. The next thing we knew we were out at sea, so spent the night on board; went back to camp with enough fish for the whole officers' mess.

Going back to the hut at night after a strike and seeing another empty bed, and having to sort out your friends' personal effects to be sent on to next-of-kin.

Waking up in the morning to find a glass of water frozen solid by your bedside. Going to the draughty W.C. outside, to find the lavatory pan just showing above a snowdrift. You were very quick!

Trying to console a weeping WAAF serving behind the bar in the officers' mess because more of us had bought it, while we drowned our own feelings in pints of beer.

Brave but very scared men. For instance, a maximum strike effort was ordered to attack a German cruiser, the *Prinz Eugen* I think it was, hiding in a small fjord. Wing Commander Bill Sise, DSO, DFC, a New Zealander and CO of 248 Squadron, was to lead us, about 36 aircraft from the three Squadrons.

The cruiser was known to have radar-controlled guns which, when they locked on to a target–finis. Heavily armed itself, extra defences had been placed all along the fjord. To make matters worse, the cloud was down, covering the tops of the mountains. So we would have to attack in straight flight under the cloud, straight up the fjord, and pull up into cloud and hopefully miss the hidden mountains behind the cruiser. Losses could be horrific.

Bill Sise, a very brave and able pilot, was nearing

the end of his briefing of the crews, when Max Aitken interrupted him from the control-room to say the strike was off–333 Squadron's recce flight had just radioed back that the weather had clamped down on the deck.

We all cheered, Bill Sise included–the relief was extraordinary. We went back to the mess and had a party. It is difficult to explain, but every one of us had accepted that they personally would very probably be going to certain death. I know Ginger Webster and I did: we admitted it over a pint along with many other crews.

T. L. Taylor, who was a navigator with 248 Squadron, commanded by Bill Sise, possesses a photograph taken in December 1944 in Flekkefjord during an attack against German ships in the harbour. In the foreground, centre, a German ship is exploding with hits; just above it and to the left can be seen a long 'flag' of white vapour, which is glycol pouring from the port engine of his Mosquito, which was being flown by Squadron Leader D. N. Robinson, the flight commander; and just above the mountainous background to the fjord, Bill Sise's aircraft is banking away after attacking.

Thus we were faced with a dead-end fjord to climb over on one engine, but the good old Merlin got us over the top and, after a rather crabby trip back over the North Sea, we arrived safely over Banff; but then our troubles began.

Probably due to the fact that only one engine was working, we had lost a great deal of hydraulic pressure and the undercarriage would not drop. So, although a belly landing was considered, I used the emergency pump and got the wheels down; but the flaps refused to budge. As you know, a Mosquito had a fairly high approach speed, so we came in

198

quickly at a slight lateral angle because of the dead engine. All was going well in spite of the cross-wind, when, for some reason which we never discovered, at the last moment full flap came down. So, instead of landing, we lifted again and were caught in the cross-wind which drifted us off the runway and across rough ground. We lost the wheels in a ditch and the tailplane on a fence and finally crashed into a small electricity building on the far side of the airfield. Here I learned the value of safety straps.

The starboard engine caught fire, so we were unable to use the door and had to exit via the escape hatch in the roof. As usual, the fire tender and the 'blood wagon' had followed us, and arrived almost at the moment we stopped. The crews were efficient, but much turning of valves, etc., only resulted in a dribble of foam dripping from the hoses. So another tender was sent for and this rapidly appeared. But instead of putting out the blaze, it caught fire itself and the aircraft, being wooden, blazed merrily away.

The next morning, all that was left was a neat, cruciform pattern of wood ash with devastated engines, guns, armour plate, etc., all sitting in the middle of it.

Nevertheless, I consider myself privileged to have flown in such a beautiful aeroplane which was justifiably called 'The Wooden Wonder'.

Mosquito crews were chosen only from the experienced–second or even third tour men. Squadron Leader G. A. B. Lord, FRAeS, had done a tour on Hudsons in the Mediterranean, often on anti-submarine work. Submarines seemed to be more visible there and he was credited with one U-boat sunk, one probably sunk, and one damaged. One German U-boat which he damaged, had also damaged his aircraft; at that time, Admiral Dönitz had only just decreed that U-boats would fight it out on the surface, using plentiful flak. 'They were not supposed to do that! And this was the first of this sort that we met. It was a good idea, because aircraft coming in to drop depth-charges and then get away, made vulnerable targets.' The submarine he definitely disposed of was Italian.

We were off Sicily and I was aft in the Elsan. You could just make a visit to the toilet and back if you put in the autopilot with the Hudson's nose slightly down. On this occasion, there were hasty signals from up front and I rushed forward without adjusting my clothing, as they say.

There was a periscope down below us. The submarine hadn't seen us, so to lose height without gaining too much speed, I put down wheels and flaps. It was perfect and we got a straddle on the periscope. For an hour afterwards, we circled the spot. There were no survivors, just a lot of oil and rubbish welling up. I thought: 'What have I done?'

Normally, it was all very impersonal because when you're flying you're detached. But now, having done it, and with everything quiet, the enormity began to sink in.

George Lord's first tour ended in 1942, then after instruction on Beaufighters in Britain he was posted to Cornwall for a second tour, and converted to Mosquitos.

I switched to 235 Squadron and moved to Banff, flying the Mosquito FB VI with four cannon, four m.gs., and four rocket rails under each wing. At first, we had the bulbous 60-lb rocket, which didn't penetrate shipping and caused little structural damage. Sometimes there were hang-ups on the rails. If that happened, you had to bail out because if you tried a landing, the thing was liable to explode.

We went over to the 23-pdr armour-piercing rocket. We delivered these at 280 knots in a shallow dive. The rails had to be set so that they were parallel with the airflow at correct diving speed, otherwise the rockets would weathercock, and either overshoot or undershoot the target; and similarly if we dived at the wrong airspeed.

We aimed for below the waterline, right down low, at a range of two to three hundred yards. That made a small hole underwater, but the partly-burnt rocket motor went on burning inside the ship while the rocket head went out the other side, making an 18-inch hole underwater while going out. In the Norwegian fjords you usually only had one chance, so you fired all eight rockets at one go.

We had two Norwegian naval aircrews with us, familiar with the coastline, who had escaped, and who carried out reconnaissance with us. Some of our information came from transmitters in Norway; the operators would put them on a bike, openly– knowing what would happen if they were caught– and push the bikes up into the mountains, often deep in snow; we heard that people would save their rations to give to the men who pushed the bikes.

The German ships used to creep down the Norwegian coast in the dark, and in daylight moor under sheer rock faces in a fjord. Our recce Mosquitos would radio back a coded signal report- ing the targets they had spotted, and we would go out to attack.

We would split into two or three groups: the first wave (say three aircraft) were anti-flak (no one relished this); the second wave (say three aircraft) were to hit the target against less opposition (hopefully); the third wave (three aircraft, if there were enough) were the top cover (for protection against enemy fighters).

As the ships were moored under the sheer rock faces, we had to make a very steep turn away after firing. Then we would scoot up the fjord hell-for-leather, and then up the mountainside. Often there were little farms at the top and I have seen people come out, waving flags. The Focke Wulf 190s waited until the attack was over and the Mossies were coming out. Damaged Mosquitos were slower, and more liable to be caught.

One trick the Germans used against us was to sling cables across the fjord. You couldn't see them. We lost our CO–Wing Commander Atkinson, an Australian–in this way. The cable just sliced a wing off.

In Coastal Command in the beginning there had been a distinct naval influence, with a tendency to equate aircraft with naval units, ignoring the realities of range. However, by the time the battleship *Tirpitz* was creeping down the Norwegian coast, she was known to be out of range of a Mosquito, '*fortunately*', remarked George Lord. Finally, 617 Squadron, the 'Dam Busters', with their four-engined Lancasters, came to Banff, waiting there for a chance to bomb the *Tirpitz* with their special, enormous armour-piercing bombs. During their wait, the Mosquitos coming back from an op let off steam by beating up the airfield, bending the DF aerials on the control tower.

I was out on an op the day the Dam Busters attacked the *Tirpitz*, and was diverted to Dallachy when I returned. On their return, the Dam Busters had tried to emulate the Mossies by a beat-up. In the course of this, a large object (one of their special bombs with a time-fuse) came out of one Lancaster and landed near the Flying Control Tower. Troops were dispersed, aircraft diverted, the airfield virtually evacuated for more than 24 hours, until the bomb could be de-fused.

For our attacks, we would fly out in the dark and aim to arrive at first light. We had one of the earliest radio altimeters which could be set for a given height to be flown at, say 50 feet. It had three lights: amber in that case meant above 50 feet, green was 50 feet, red was below 50 feet. With the long North Sea swells, you could see them recorded by the lights. When we heard the enemy jamming our radios, we knew we had been detected. Then we climbed up and went into the fjord in close battle formation.

One scheme proposed was for a Warwick aircraft (a modified Wellington) to be out there in the dark, waiting for us to arrive, and laying a circle of flares on the sea, perhaps a mile in diameter. We had to keep radio silence, we were dispersed, and it was dark; but we were supposed to identify each other by the light of the flares. That was telling the enemy! Must have been thought up by a chap deep underground.

On 15 October, 1944, what was planned was an operation involving both Mosquitos with rockets and Torbeaus (Beaufighters with torpedos).

Just south of Christiansand, going west from Germany, was a ship of some importance, for it was escorted by flak-ships, balloon-ships and ships with parachute-and-cable devices. We reckoned we hit her on the stern with a 500-lb bomb, but I think the destruction was caused by a torpedo. One minute the ship was there, then there was just an expanding cloud of smoke–a ring of fire over the sea–and in there were human beings with not a hope of surviving. Normally, one felt detached. This was one of the few occasions when I felt differently. It was probably a munition ship or tanker.

In early 1945 there were successful attacks by Mosquitos on U-boats. Our claims were pretty near the reality. We sank 300,000 tons of shipping, with losses comparable to those of Bomber Command and sometimes much higher, but we were cost-effective. 700 aircrew were involved–65 per cent were killed, 250 aircraft lost.

The Merlin 25s in the Mark VI fighter-bomber Mosquito were liquid-cooled engines; one bullet through the cooling system and the engine was out of action, whereas the air-cooled Hercules radials in the Beaufighter could take a little more punishment.

The Mosquito was ahead of its time but it was not a forgiving aircraft. However, it had such a good performance that it was exploited by the Air Staff, who loaded it up with rockets, long-range tanks, two drop-tanks, bombs, and so on, which impaired the handling qualities and the performance.

At 8 OTU, Haverfordwest, I saw a Mosquito break up in the circuit. It just came apart behind the trailing edge. The tail unit fluttered down, but the cockpit and wings rotated as they fell, burning to death the two chaps in the cockpit. There were a few mysterious ones, such as the Mossie which was firing rockets at targets moored in the sea, with an AOC from Group watching from the clifftop. The Mossie just went in. An aileron had come adrift, because a hinge-nut had no split-pin. All aircraft were grounded for inspection and other cases found. They had all been made at some shadow factory.

Bill Clayton-Graham's log continues into the New Year, 1945, with the war in its closing stages; and Norway becoming a bolthole for German surface ships and submarines as Reich territory contracted. On 21 February Clayton-Graham went to Leirvik again, with eight

Mosquitos, to attack two small ships of 1,500 and 500 tons, which both sank. It was the first time he had used the rocket projectiles. They were effective, but his photographs were of poor quality.

On 17 March excellent pictures were taken of an attack against six ships in Aalesund harbour by 31 strike aircraft escorted by 12 Mustangs.

As the harbour was very heavily defended, two aircraft of the Norwegian 333 Squadron led us in overland south of the harbour. The first photo shows us approaching the coast on the deck, the height we always flew at across the North Sea on leaving Banff. The second and third photos were taken as we flew over the mountains, so we could attack with the minimum prior warning.

There were four ships in the outer harbour and two in the inner harbour, the latter being shown in my photos. I attacked the 6,000-ton ship on the left. The photo-sequence shows me opening up with machine-guns, firing cannons, my RPs on their way and finally the RPs hitting spot on. My ship and two others sank; the other three ships were crippled. There was a lot of flak and we lost two aircraft.

On 23 March the target was a troopship, the 7,800-ton *Rothenfels*, anchored at the end of Dalsfjord. Nine Mosquitos attacked, seven returned.

Guns had been taken off the ship and mounted on both sides of the narrow fjord, so we had to attack from over the end of the fjord in line astern and fly through a heavy crossfire of light flak. We were led in overland to the target by 333 Squadron. Our strike leader, S/Ldr Robbie Read, was shot down plus one other. I took over and brought the remaining aircraft home. The ship was left burning.

The next sequence of photographs was taken in Porsgrund harbour on 30 March. The most striking shows a black cloud of smoke curling up just beyond the quayside. This was Flight Lieutenant Bill Knowles' Mosquito, which hit the pylons and went in. There were four merchant ships, of which three sank at their moorings, the fourth being badly damaged; a warehouse full of chemicals was also destroyed. As this was a heavily defended area, eight aircraft went ahead to attack gun emplacements, followed by 32 aircraft of the strike force using RPs. Two Mosquitos were lost.

On 5 April, 37 strike aircraft attacked, with a Mustang escort, a widely spread-out convoy in the Kattegat, after flying across Denmark.

The ships were heavily armed but all were left on fire and sinking, and it was reported later that more than 200 bodies of German soldiers were picked up from the sea by Swedish boats, with an estimated total of 900 troops lost. We lost three aircraft out of the 37.

A sequence of six photographs records this action. But for the next operation, on 9 April, unfortunately Clayton-Graham's Mosquito was fitted only with a ciné camera, so he has no stills.

A strike force of 31 aircraft led by S/Ldr Bert Gunnis, equipped with RPs, and with five other Mosquitos giving fighter cover, attacked three U-boats in the Skaggerak. They were all sunk.* My aircraft was hit by pieces of submarine as my cannon and rockets went in. We lost three aircraft out of the 31.

And again on 2 May, 1945, another strike by 27

* U-804, U-843, U-1065.

aircraft on two U-boats in the Kattegat, resulting in one being sunk† and the other a probable, for the loss of one aircraft.

On the afternoon of that day, the Elbe Line was breached and at dawn on 3 May, the message through the headsets of the advancing British armour was: 'In Hamburg all resistance has ceased.' Effectively, the war in Europe was over.

But the war in the Far East was far from over. One scheme involving Mosquitos carrying an unusual weapon bridged the two theatres of war (and was kept secret until long after the war). 618 Squadron was formed in April 1943, equipped with Mosquito IVs (a month before 617 Squadron, equipped with Lancasters, carried out the Dams raid). They were to carry a rounded bouncing bomb, which would skip across the water over the net defences which surrounded major warships in port, and which, striking the ship's side, would sink to a lethal depth before exploding. You have to be very careful where you put your feet on a modern warship, in case you kick the plating in, but battleships weren't built like that–they had heavily-armoured sides and massive armoured decks–the only unarmoured part being well below the waterline. The problem was not unlike that involved in breaching a dam. The bouncing bombs devised by Dr Barnes Wallis for the Möhne, Sorpe and Eder dams had the code name of 'Upkeep'; the smaller ones designed to be carried, two at a time, in the belly of a Mosquito were called 'Highball'. Their target was to be the *Tirpitz*, then moored in Astenfiord, and the date of the attack was to be 15 May, 1943, because the *Tirpitz* needed to be sunk now if not before, in order to have much effect on the war. But testing took too long, for the bombs which had 600-lb warheads, had to be spun by a rotor and dropped at 25

† U-2359.

feet, so that they would skip over the water like a thrown stone.

When the snags had been ironed out, aircrews were given operational postings to bring them up to date with current strike practice. This resulted in the death of the CO, Squadron Leader C. F. Rose, DFC, who was killed while flying a Tsetse Mosquito with the 57-mm gun with 248 Squadron.

By now, *Tirpitz* had been put out of action by midget submarines and strike forces operating from aircraft carriers (although she was not actually capsized by Barnes Wallis's special 12,000 lb bombs until November). So in July 1944 a new anti-warship role was planned for 618 Squadron and the Highballs, in a scheme code-named 'Oxtail'. They were to join a force of British aircraft carriers in the Pacific, operating against Japan. They became the first carrier-based Mosquito squadron, and their destination now was Australia.

CHAPTER FOURTEEN
Far East
(1943-1945)

LAC F. Dyer, an RAF fitter-armourer, was posted to the Far East in 1943 and eventually joined 82 Squadron during its conversion from American Vultee Vengeance dive-bombers to Mosquitos.

> On joining the squadron at Kolar in India, I was greeted by Warrant Officer Warren, a Londoner from Croydon. His first words to me were:
> 'Get rid of your kitbag, lad, then report back here, and *jillo* (hurry up).'
> On my return, he ordered me to climb up onto a lorry that was standing by. Little did I know that I was on a burial party. One of our planes had crashed, killing the pilot and navigator, and I was to help bury them. That was my initation into 82 Squadron, a great one at that.

It was some months before aircrews and ground crews had got the feel of FB Mark IVs, and then they moved to Kumbhirgram in Assam, a journey which took the ground crews five days by train.

> We soon settled down in our new home and within days our aircraft were operational, mostly strafing and bombing various Jap targets. Friendships between aircrews and us were fantastic. Surnames were hardly ever used.
> We had many good evenings in our armourers'

basha (hut). A portable HMV gramophone was the means of entertainment. Two of our great mates were always invited to these sessions–W/O Vic Empson, a pilot, and his navigator, W/O Ted Allanack. Often they would manage to bring a bottle of gin, and we would sit on our *charpoys* (beds) listening to records of various bands.

Assam was a very hot and humid place, malaria was rife; fortunately, all I caught was dysentry. Our airstrip was on a kind of plateau, with jungle either side. Re-arming and bombing-up the aircraft was hard work, but satisfaction achieved at the end. Compared to the 14th Army, we were well off.

I vividly recall an incident that happened while I was re-arming one of our aircraft. I heard engines being revved up at the far end of the runway, and instantly recognised it to be a Beaufighter. It roared up the runway, lifting off opposite where I was working. It then veered to starboard and plunged down into the jungle. It had been on a test flight after an engine overhaul; the pilot and engine-fitter aboard never stood a chance.

I also remember one of our aircraft returning badly shot up, the navigator dying of head wounds the next day.

One day the squadron took off to bomb a brothel in Mandalay. Intelligence had found out that high-ranking Japanese officers were using this brothel at a certain time every morning. So we obliged by catching them on the job.

When Mandalay fell to the 14th Army, we uprooted once again and flew down to a paddy-field airstrip not far from Cox's Bazaar in the Arakan, Rangoon being still occupied by the Japanese.

After this the Squadron was pulled back to India, in preparation for the planned invasion of Malaya, which has the great naval base of Singapore at its south-eastern tip. Dyer and his comrades set about converting the Mosquitos to take rockets; but Dyer himself was shortly after repatriated to Britain, as many others were at this time because they had spent so many years cut off from home, without home leave, in a climate uncongenial, to say the least. But, not only was the climate hostile to Europeans, it was hostile also to some of their artefacts, especially the Mosquito, made of timber and plywood and heat-bonded by glues.

Robert Smith, a Beaufighter pilot, was posted in March 1945 to 89 Squadron at Baigachi in Bengal, about 26 miles from Calcutta.

They were using Beaufighters and it was intended that 89 would transfer to Mosquitos, a number of which had been despatched to the airfield. During the conversion a number of inexplicable accidents occurred, one of which proved fatal, and as a result all the planes were grounded.

Eventually Geoffrey de Havilland arrived at the squadron and it transpired that the planes had been constructed in Canada and the manufacturers had used a different adhesive from the British version, in the pressing of the plywood, which was not as resistant to the effects of the Indian heat; with the result that certain parts under stress during flight began to delaminate, causing distortion. This of course affected the flying characteristics of the plane. Apart from this, we were pretty pleased with the aircraft.

Mike Morgan, who was photographic officer for two PRU Squadrons in Malaya in 1945–681 (Spitfires) and 684 (Mosquitos) recalled:

A couple of Mossies lost their wings in mid-air. As

a result, all Mossies were grounded, except those of 684 Squadron, which came direct from De Havilland's, Hatfield.

I tremble to think of the number of people I bored to distraction, extolling the virtues of this magnificent flying machine. Its elegance and efficiency inspired confidence and elation on every take-off. You pounded down the strip, pushed back in your seat, moulded to it–you became part of its structure.

The pilots I knew (I was not a pilot) all seemed to have the same technique (rightly or wrongly). Having reached a speed that one felt was the ultimate, they pulled the aircraft off the deck rather sharply–and you were *really* flying! Even in these days of pressurised cabins and jet engines, take-off is not quite the same.

In retrospect, one has to admit that the confidence one felt was helped by the fact that the Mosquito PR plane was the fastest aircraft in that area–a great help if you ran into trouble.

As you know, the PR Mosquito had no armament, but was full of cameras, not least two long focal-length cameras mounted at an angle for overlap and wide coverage; and in those days, that meant a very tall camera.

Mike Morgan's PR units were covering the Allied advance from Burma and Malaya towards Singapore. Similar PR Mosquitos were based in Australia. At first known as the No. 1 PRU, they were based initially in the Northern Territory of Australia. The area they had to cover was vast: the Dutch East Indies, including East Java, Borneo East, the Celebes, the Halmahera Islands, Timor and Kai Islands. They were to seek and photograph Japanese airfields, naval bases and army installations; to track naval and merchant shipping movements; and to map selected areas when required. This area was soon extended to cover the Philippine Islands–and in particular Davao Gulf and Leyte Gulf where Japanese Army build-ups were suspected–as well as movements of the Japanese Navy

The Mosquito FB Mark 40 was modified at the request of the Royal Australian Air Force to carry two F24 split-vertical cameras and an F52 vertical camera mounted in the bomb-bay. Two extra fuel tanks of 126 gallons capacity were fitted in the bomb-bay and the doors sealed; two drop tanks were added for a total fuel load of 865 gallons.

The first of these modified aircraft was flown on an operational sortie on 1 June, 1944 from the Coomalie Creek airstrip some 54 miles south of Darwin. On 10 September, 1945 No. 1 PRU was reformed as No. 86 (Photographic Reconnaissance) Squadron, RAAF, equipped with Mosquito Mark 40s, and was later to receive Mosquito Mark XVIs from Britain. The aircrews were chosen from those who had served overseas and had completed operational tours, together with RAAF pilots who had amassed high flying hours or who had already served in reconnaissance units. Conversions to Mosquitos were carried out at Williamstown in New South Wales.

During these operations the Mosquitos encountered severe tropical storms and cyclones, and continuously had to contend with the 'intertropic front'; the leading edges of the mainplanes had to be modified to enable the aircraft to survive the impact of these tropical storms.

With the increase in men and equipment, much more activity was expected of the Squadron. The intention was that the United States Air Force would be relieved of its reconnaissance role from North-Western Australia. The aircraft were expected to operate to the limit of their range and from forward airfields when required, so as to increase this range. In order to reach targets in East Java, where major Japanese installations existed, the airstrip at Broome in Western Australia, some 1,500 miles from

Coomalie Creek, was used. This enabled Mark 40 aircraft to reach targets in East Java, and many sortie times of eight hours plus were recorded by these aircraft. The longest flight recorded from Broome to East Java was 2,300 miles in a flight of nine hours' duration.

The Squadron took delivery of more of the modified Mark 40s, but in March 1945 it took delivery of the first of a batch of twelve Mark XVI (PRU) Mosquitos from Britain. The Mark XVI cruised at faster speeds than the Mark 40, but it used more fuel, so it was restricted to shorter-range operations.

During operations, it was discovered that if aircraft were flown from airstrips founded on crushed coral or sand, fine particles would be sucked into the air-intakes, and after some hours there was a silicon build-up on the plug points which caused engine failure. Rolls Royce and De Havilland representatives, working with the engineers of 87 Squadron, modified the intakes and succeeded in reducing the incidence of engine failure from this cause. Nevertheless, this phenomenon had interesting results for some of the aircrews.

An instance occurred on 27 February, 1945, involving Squadron Leader K. J. 'Red' Gray, of Sydney and his navigator, Flying Officer W.E. 'Bill' Sudlow of Perth, Western Australia. They were detailed to fly from Coomalie Creek airstrip to Broome in Western Australia, on the first leg of an operational sortie to East Java and the island of Bali. Gray tells what happened.

We were airborne from Broome at first light (5.30 a.m.) on 25 February. The airstrip was adequate but care had to be taken with a fully-laden aircraft, particularly when there was no wind, because the over-run consisted of a sandy surface with sand dunes situated at the end of it–after that there was nothing but sea. The ocean beach which stretches from Broome in a south-westerly direction is known as 85 mile beach–being unbroken for that distance.

The prime operational targets in East Java were the military installations and airfield at Malang, followed by Banjoewangi Harbour at the eastern tip of Java, and a reconnaissance of Bali on the return leg.

The weather on the outward leg consisted of unbroken cloud below us, with indications of storms because of cloud altitudes. The 'intertropic front' was encountered 200 miles south of landfall, and was evidently very active, because we had to thread our way through the then towering cloud formations, which would still further build up later in the day. Our operational height was 21,000 feet, and the weather over the target was excellent. While carrying out the necessary photographic runs, the starboard engine overheated and failed. Two more runs were needed to complete the task and we then began to make our way to Banjoewangi Harbour as this was more or less on the way back.

We photographed the harbour at some 1,200 feet and carried on to Bali, losing height because there was no possibility of flying through the 'intertropic front', and certainly not on one motor. Just south of the island of Bali, the port motor cut out, and Bill radioed a Mayday stating our then known position.

With the starboard motor we lost the electrical generator, so that there was no radio after we had sent the distress calls, and therefore we couldn't get any acknowledgments. In the meantime, the port motor started again and seemed to settle down, so we decided to try and make Broome, as opposed to ditching in the sea or crash-landing on a Japanese-held island. We were to learn later that the Mayday call had been received and that submarines had been alerted and sent to the area.

The return journey had to be flown just above the sea in order to get under the 'intertropic front' and the storms which covered the return track. The weather turned out to be atrocious and visibility in the tropical storms was appalling, but there was no turning back once we had negotiated the main front. After five hours plus we reckoned we must hit Australia since it was a large enough target. We had deliberately navigated north, so that we could then follow the coastline in a southerly direction to Broome, with the knowledge that we could probably land or ditch on or near a beach if necessary. As it was, when we sighted the general coastline, the port motor decided to overheat and fail, and there was nothing to do but ditch.

As luck would have it, a small island appeared out of a squall and that became the ditching target. We had gone through ditching drills during our journey back, and I suppose we had thought of everything we could do in the event of it being necessary.

The aircraft touched down on the sea very well because the noise of the flaps being torn away on impact was clearly audible before the aircraft finally entered the water and nosed down. Bill, opening the hatch and releasing the aircraft dinghy simultaneously at the moment of touch-down, was thrown forward by the impact but was not seriously hurt and was able to scramble out on to the wing. I was caught with my right leg in the rudder pedal because of having to offset the swing of the aircraft when we lost the power of the second motor. I had activated the flaps when the decision was taken to ditch and we still had some motor power.

The aircraft nosed down and Bill had to pull me free from the cockpit, but the aircraft, because of empty tank buoyancy, did not at that time sink by

216

the nose any further, but rather settled with the cockpit full of water; this enabled us to stand on the wing and release our parachute dinghies. Bill did some cockpit diving, while I held his heels, for as many bits and pieces as we could retrieve. We were anxious to retrieve our full water-bottle because we both knew of the reputation of Western Australia for survival without water . . . But it actually rained every day for another week!

We now had the aircraft two-man dinghy and the two parachute dinghies in the sea, and mobilised them into a convoy with all the spare bits in one of the smaller ones. The aircraft had settled a little more by now, but we were able to gain access to the belly and began removing the camera-magazine and any salvageable items associated with the camera. The aircraft's attitude became more vertical, so this idea was given up, and we began to paddle towards the island some 300 yards away. When within about 30 yards from it, the tide began to recede and we were swept out to sea with a riptide current—we later learned these rips could be well in excess of 10 knots. The tide in the region of Broome and King Sound rises and falls over 30 feet, and the whirlpools and rips are quite awe-inspiring, especially when you are in a dinghy!

The aircraft was last seen floating out to sea like ourselves, with its nose down and the tail almost vertical. We never did see it sink, because we were soon in the middle of a storm in the open sea.

That night was spent in a howling gale, rain and huge seas, but the following morning the weather had abated somewhat and we could make out land some 300 or 400 yards away. However, we were not able to get any closer before we were again swept out to sea for the next twenty-four hours. At first light on the second day, we found we had drifted

217

towards some submerged mangrove trees, towards which we paddled, and when among them we lashed the dinghies to the tree-tops. As the tide receded, we were left stranded on black mud in the middle of the mangrove swamp with a sandy shore some 250 yards away.

After establishing that the mud was knee deep and that it needed all our strength to make progress, we abandoned the dinghies and everything which we could not carry in one load, because we realised that it was a 'one way' journey with another change of tide to contend with. We managed to make the shore after some hours' effort, constantly urged on by the thought of the incoming tide . . .

The rest of the day was spent in rest and discussion as to where we might be in relation to Broome. Bill Sudlow, being a native of Perth, reckoned that we could ultimately reach his home town if we kept going south–a mere 2,000 miles!

Drinking water and thirst were constant concerns and we did everything to conserve the former, even to fashioning a water-bag out of the rubber shroud of the aircraft dinghy for storing and carrying rain water. And it rained for the next week . . .

We lived off the land, eating such things as lizards, birds' eggs, crabs, etc., and even tried out our .38 service pistols on some kangaroos, to no avail. From the emergency packs we managed to salvage some dry matches so that we could build a fire for cooking and drying out. On the third day's walk we stumbled on an aborigine with his wife, in their small camp–we saw the smoke of his fire, on which he was roasting the haunches of a kangaroo. We turned over all our emergency rations to them and ate all theirs–and drank their tea.

They undertook to lead us to the Lombardino Mission Station, which turned out to be some seven hours' forced march from where they were camped. The Mission was reached in the evening, when we were greeted by the German-Australian Brother and some nuns who ran it; they had heard rumours from the natives that 'birdmen' had landed in the water, but had no details whatsoever. We were fed, our cuts and scratches were cleaned up–we were given cigarettes and some four-star medicinal brandy, and put to bed in hospital beds in a schoolroom.

We were informed that the RAAF had a radio station detachment some 20 miles away, and a runner was despatched with a note to inform them of our whereabouts. We were taken to their head-quarters and a Tiger Moth was summoned from Broome, some ninety miles south-west of their base at Cape Levique, to fly us to Broome. After a short sojourn in hospital for a check-up and treatment for our cuts and scratches, which were beginning to react to mangrove mud, etc., we were returned to the Squadron some nine days after our sortie began.

From March 1945 Mark XVIs were used almost exclusively by 87 Squadron, but the Mark 40s were still used to fly the extreme range missions to Java and East Borneo. (The De Havilland factory at Bankstown in Australia produced several hundred Mosquitos during the war, including the Mark 40s.)

Also in March, it was suspected that the Japanese heavy cruiser *Isuzu*, with three escorts, was on the move towards Koepang in Timor island. 87 Squadron flew a number of sorties to find them and successfully photographed the warships in spite of Oscar fighters attempting to intercept the Mosquitos. The squadron shadowed them until they were attacked by Liberators and Mitchells of the RAAF. In spite of losses, the bombers hit the cruiser three times; it was later sunk by US submarines and the escorts were dispersed.

In June 1945, at the request of Lord Louis Mountbatten, supreme commander of South East Asia Command, three Mosquitos from 87 Squadron were sent on detachment to RAF Station Brown, which was in the Cocos Islands in the Indian Ocean, some 1,600 nautical miles from the nearest airfield of Learmouth in Western Australia. This was classified 'Top Secret' and the three crews selected were given sealed orders, to open after take-off, to proceed to Learmouth airfield on Exmouth Gulf, where they would receive further instructions. This was a five-hour flight. Once at Learmouth, the crews were briefed to fly to the Cocos Islands and were given US Air Corps charts of the Pacific area showing the Cocos.

An amphibious landing force had recently got ashore unopposed on the Cocos and a base was being set up which included an airstrip capable of mounting full-scale operations against Japanese bases in the Dutch East Indies and Singapore, which were much nearer from here than they were from Australia. At this time, the strip could take Mosquitos, and an RAF Spitfire squadron had also just flown in. The longer-range Mosquitos were to photograph Singapore and adjacent installations from the south, and to feed information to SEAC and the Pacific Command. The three Australian crews were Squadron Leader K. J. 'Red' Gray, now with the DFC, and his navigator 'Bill' Sudlow (Mentioned in Despatches), recovered from their ditching. Also flying a Mark XVI were Flight Lieutenant R. H. 'Ron' Langsford, DFC, and Flying Officer G. 'Tom' Tozer. The single Mark 40 was crewed by Flight Lieutenant A. L. M. 'Art' Spurgin, DFC, and Flying Officer L. C. 'Lennie' Lobb.

RAF Brown operated VHF control and homing, but there was no W/T communication available, and the crews' instructions were clear that W/T silence was to be observed throughout the flight from Learmouth to the

Cocos. Based on meteorological briefing and dead reckoning, the flying time was estimated at five hours–which meant that in the event of location problems the flight would have to rely on VHF homing, as there could be no return. Because of the high priority of the mission, combined with the experience of the aircrews, the risk was thought reasonable, and at the time no concern was voiced.

The weather was predicted to be fair throughout; and indeed it was excellent until ETA approached; and then it began to deteriorate. At the time of rendezvous, visibility had dropped to zero from sea level to 20,000 feet. The point of no return had been passed and so W/T silence was broken. VHF communications deteriorated also; the aircraft could not contact each other and only one of them was able to hear the VHF controller on Cocos. Unsuccessful efforts were made to home Cocos on the strength of that voice transmission. But after almost eight hours in the air fuel was exhausted, and Langsford and Tozer indicated that they were reaching the limit and would break formation to go below and ditch.

Meanwhile, RAF Brown had reacted to the crisis, firstly by sending out sections of Spitfires to look for the Mosquitos; and secondly, by erecting and operating a W/T Directional Finding Station from the equipment which had just been unloaded from the ships. As Langsford broke formation to go down below cloud for ditching, the W/T ground station made contact and gave a rough bearing to steer. Langsford followed it and so did the other two Mosquitos. Then, almost at once, a Spitfire of 136 Squadron, RAF, flown by Flight Lieutenant G. A. Macdonald, chanced upon the two Mosquitos at 23,000 feet above cloud. He was able to lead them in for some 80 miles, on more or less the course on which they were heading, enabling them to make a landing on the steel strip. Gray's Mark XVI fuel gauges indicated zero. This Mosquito had been airborne for eight hours and twenty-five minutes.

In the meantime, Langsford and Tozer had broken cloud. Right ahead of them was a coral outcrop in the sea, on which they made a successful belly landing. The outcrop was known as North Island and was some 15 miles from the main Cocos group. A section of Spitfires found the missing Mosquito and its crew at about 1700 hours that day.

Later, examining again the US Service maps they had used for the trip, they established that the latitudinal and longitudinal position of the Cocos islands shown was some 65 miles from that shown on British Admiralty charts. But this was only a contributory cause for missing the islands, because the search flown by the Mosquitos would have found Cocos had the weather been at all favourable. Gray commented:

I'm glad I didn't have to push my luck by ditching a Mosquito a second time. All the credit for avoiding a total disaster must be given to the RAF for creating their packing-case W/T radio station and the subsequent homing feat, plus the 136 Squadron Spitfire pilots who wouldn't give up their search. Their efforts prevented a disastrous ending to what was the first co-operative operational effort between the RAF of South East Asia Command and the RAAF in the South Pacific area.

But bad weather prevailed over the Cocos Islands and the Indian Ocean while the detachment was at RAF Brown; and only one operational sortie was flown, to Christmas Island–not Singapore as intended.

The Australian Mosquitos were replaced by RAF ones from 684 Squadron. Serving in this detachment as a navigator was Warrant Officer H. S. Painter, a former schoolmaster at Enderby House, Narborough; his pilot was Squadron Leader Cliff Andrews, DFC, of the Royal

222

New Zealand Air Force. Painter's log shows a number of sorties over Singapore, including one on 4 August (two days before the first A-Bomb exploded over Hiroshima). On 9 August the Nagasaki bomb exploded and on 15 August the Japanese government accepted the Allied terms for surrender. Tens of thousands of Allied soldiers were near death in the Japanese POW camps and their associated work parties, and General Slim, the British commander in Burma and Malaya, was anxious to rescue them as soon as possible. The Japanese reaction to their defeat might take the form of revenge. On 19 August, however, his plans to take over control suffered from a 'spanner in the works'. The Allied Chiefs of Staff had authorised General McArthur to mount a spectacular Japanese surrender in Tokyo Bay, with battleships and all the trimmings; until then no one was to land or re-enter the outlying territories where most of the camps were. The date was fixed for 31 August, and then deferred until 2 September, when the show was staged which officially ended the war with Japan (although not all Japanese recognised the fact). This is the necessary background to an unusually full entry in Painter's log for 31 August, which is an exceptional two-and-a-half lines long and reads:

Cocos–Singapore. (Std. engine u/s, landed Singapore. Friendly reception by Japs. POWs contacted. Engine repaired by POW!)

As with most log entries (usually one-line affairs) this hardly tells the story, but he later gave his family a fuller version. His son recalls:

My father always said that they had no option but to put down at Singapore (one engine being out of action). They landed without trouble, although they had feared the worst, because the previous sortie

223

had been the first occasion on which, after the Japanese surrender on 15 August, they had met anti-aircraft fire. His story went that as they opened the inner hatch to disembark, the Japanese ground staff opened the outer! He and his pilot had decided to disembark wearing their revolvers (he always swore that everyone in 684 Squadron carried a .45, regardless of the Geneva Convention, for its stopping power). They were 'helped' to disembark but not disarmed. Indeed it appeared that the 'tarmac' welcoming party included officers complete with swords; there was much bowing and heel-clicking. At length they were taken to what appeared to be the officers' mess and were dined, their revolver holsters draped over their chair-backs! I believe their overnight stop may have been at Changi, but cannot be certain. At all events, POWs repaired their engine and they were allowed to take off next day and returned to Cocos.

Changi was of course the infamous POW camp which at around this time had the famous message painted on its roof: 'JAPS GONE–EXTRACT DIGIT'.

A letter home to his wife prompted the press to proclaim Painter and his pilot the first men into Singapore: a claim which Painter publicly denied:

A British medical officer had parachuted into the country to attend to prisoners-of-war the previous day. He was the first man in, but my pilot, Sqdn.-Ldr. Cliff Andrews, a New Zealander, and myself were the first men to land a kite in Singapore.

And what of 618 Squadron and their secret 'Highball' weapon, the bouncing bomb, who were to wage war on Japanese shipping from a British carrier force? On 29 June, 1945, they were disbanded, probably because the

American government had decided that the Pacific was to be 'manifestly' an all-American sphere of influence. For security reasons, the weapon being regarded as effective, the 'Highballs' brought out to the Far East were destroyed, and nearly two decades were to pass before details of them were released.

225

CHAPTER FIFTEEN
Peace
(1945-1955)

Ron Browne joined the RAF in June 1941, was trained in the USA, and on return to Britain was told he and one other pilot were to become instructors. Both men were indignant and protested to the CO. First, however, they had to do a seven-week course of flying instruction, and Ron hit on the idea of giving the CO a 'terrible ride' when it came to the test for final grading. It didn't work. The CO simply said: 'If you think you've failed, you haven't. We know you can do it. So better make your mind up. I'm passing you!'

That was in May, 1943. Nearly two years later Browne's stint was over, and there was some choice of what to fly, a tour as instructor, like an operational tour, allowing an application for Mosquitos.

Nobody wanted heavy bombers. Everybody wanted Mossies, because the Mossie was the Rolls Royce of the air. So I put in for Mosquitos, and got it.

My first flight in a Mossie was on 10 April 1945. In May I was posted to 142 Squadron in 8 Group, the Pathfinders. But the war in Europe ended before I could do an op. Then we all got inoculated to go out to Malaya; and *that* was packed up. So I went back to instructing.

On 13 August, 1945, Browne made a ferry flight from Gransden Lodge to Upwood near Cambridge; as it was only a short flight, he did not need a navigator.

The Mosquito had unpleasant characteristics on landing. It swung to port, badly. It landed at about 120 mph and many of the runways were short, 1,500 yards or so. If you were landing on a 1,500-yard runway, and the Mossie swung, you couldn't use opposite engine to straighten up, because there wasn't room to stop before the end of the runway was reached; so you had to use opposite brake. But sometimes the Mossie went sideways–then the oleo struts would collapse. So the drill was: just let it run off the concrete onto the grass, if it didn't straighten. Of course, on a 2,000-yard runway there was no problem, the extra distance to travel let you use opposite engine.

When I came in to land on this particular 1,500-yard runway, she swung to port; so I applied starboard brake. But she didn't straighten, so I let the aircraft go off the runway. What I didn't know was that there was a hollow by the side of an adjoining runway. That wiped the undercarriage completely off and ripped the belly straight out.

BANG! The machine went straight down.

Now, on a Mossie your feet are ahead of the props–and I believe a number of people had their feet chopped off at the ankles when the broken propellors came through the fuselage. So, the idea was to get your feet back quick.

On this occasion the prop did come through and actually cut the welt of my left shoe. As I went out through the top canopy, I saw the nose and the instrument panel just shattering. All this in a second or so. I had moved quickly, knowing what was going to happen. The machine had only just stopped, the prop blades snapping immediately. The Mossie had ended up on an adjoining runway, so probably went only 20–30 yards.

The MO came dashing round in the blood wagon:

227

'Where's the pilot?'

'I'm the pilot.'

'I never saw anyone get out of anything like that before! Any broken bones or bruises?'

They took me in the wagon and I had a full check-up, but they found absolutely nothing at all. Then they sent me back to Gransden Lodge in a Land-Rover. The Mossie was being delivered to their CO at Upwood. It was the worst one we'd got and we were glad to get rid of it.

I didn't report in immediately to the Office at Gransden Lodge, and was walking back to my hut when I saw my navigator coming towards me. He went white as a sheet and swayed, thinking he was seeing a ghost.

'What's the matter?' I asked.

'It's not you, is it?' he replied. I had been reported killed in the crash.

Browne did not feel that the Mossie was fragile, and delighted in its performance.

'We used to fly around American Flying Fortresses on one engine. They'd get annoyed.'

One entirely heretical view of RAF landing technique was expressed by a most experienced instructor and test pilot, who had flown more than 100 aircraft types and, in particular, twenty marks of Mosquito. He was not anxious to be identified because RAF flying techniques, as is well known, were not devised by mortal men and therefore cannot be questioned. But he did question them.

The three-point landing concept was responsible for 50 per cent of the swings on landing experienced with the Mossie and the Beau. If runways are long enough for wheel-landings, the safest way to land is to put down on two wheels, and then drop the tail-wheel. At night, I always put a Mosquito down on two points, given adequate runway length. You could guarantee a good wheel-landing every time. Had we taught wheel-landings, it would have cut the accident rate. A rumble landing with a put-down on two points was the safest procedure. Even if you did swing, the result was not so disastrous as with three-point.

A contrary opinion was expressed by Jeremy Howard-Williams, who had learned from John Cunningham.

John Cunningham was a De Havilland apprentice before the war and their Chief Test Pilot afterwards; he commanded No. 85 Squadron with Mosquitos from January 1943 to February 1944. In 1941, as flight commander of No. 604 Squadron (Beau-fighters at the time), he evaluated the Mosquito as a night-fighter. He took the opposite view on wheelies as opposed to three-pointers, his teaching being to make a glide approach (no throttle), pull out and drop onto three points just over the hedge (and woe betide you if you consistently erred). You were then never likely to be caught out by engine failure on the approach, or by aircraft damage causing the need for excessive power. I quote him: 'It's better to be pulled alive out of the far hedge, than dug out of the near one. 'Incidentally, the comments on the Mosquito's tendency to swing on landing is the first I have ever heard of this trait. We never swung on our glide approach and three-point landings.

A point to register against the aircraft (to make up for my defence of its landing qualities) is that of the cockpit layout–it didn't approach the Beau for efficiency. There was that unbroken row of eight or nine switches on the starboard side; how was the pilot to select the correct one in the dark? There must have been occasions when nav lights were lit instead of the gunsight . . . If they had been broken up into mini-rows of three as in the Beau, there would have been no problem. Then some of the controls were awkward, you had to change hands; and of course the pilot had to sit with legs slightly slanted to the right, which became uncomfortable after a few hours.

It was certainly a strong aircraft. I can cite the case of a Mosquito chased by a 190. The pilot turned so sharply that the aircraft did a flick (high-speed) stall accidentally, which reversed his direction and so temporarily lost his pursuer. When the 190 caught up again, this time the Mosquito pilot did a flick stall on purpose, and got away again. You see aerobatic biplanes do it at air shows, but they are specially built for this; the Mosquito wasn't, but it did.

After the war, the Mosquito acquired some new, peacetime roles. J. E. L. Gover who, with 692 Squadron, had taken 4,000-lb bombs to Berlin in 1944, was posted to 162 Squadron in October, 1945. Their job, using the Mosquitos as mini-airliners, was to carry diplomatic mail in their bomb-bays to cities like Athens, Copenhagen, Naples, Rome and Vienna; and also newspapers for the British troops serving in the different countries.

The Royal Canadian Air Force ran a daily courier service from Nuremberg, where most of the War Crimes Trials were taking place, to Odiham in the south of England. W. E. Cawthorne was glad of it.

There was an arrangement whereby they carried one man per day home on leave from the small British delegation at the war trials. I was stationed in Nuremberg, in the Royal Signals, throughout the trials and was lucky enough to be flown home on leave on two occasions in the bomb-bay of a

230

Mosquito. It certainly beat a two-day train trip.

Den Hodder joined 85 Squadron after the war, first at Tangmere and then at West Malling.

Once a year, we went to Lübeck for two or three months. In 1948, the time of the Berlin Airlift, the freight aircrews would joke, when asked where they'd been: 'We got lost over Russia.' From Lübeck, we used to fly all over Europe and we did indeed get lost over the Russian Zone of Germany, because it was just beyond the end of the runway, so to speak.

I remember flying over Hamburg. Hundreds of ships sunk in the docks. Then I visited Hamburg by train and throughout the city saw mile upon mile of devastation.

Once–I'd come out that day from England–I saw a sight that stuck in my mind. A crowd of people– off a refugee train?–was shuffling down the platform. In rags. Living skeletons. Virtually zombies. Remember, I'd been in England a few hours before.

The squadron was engaged on night-fighter training using radar and navigational aids, going out at about ten at night and coming back around two or three in the morning.

'The Mossie was a lovely aircraft, with a distinctive tone to the engines. You could always tell a Mossie coming in by the sound.

'Wing Commander S. McCreith, AFC, MRAeS, had ended his operational flying career in October 1944, when he was hit by 88-mm flak over Hungary and crash-landed near Lake Balaton.

Thereafter I was an unwilling guest of the Third Reich. After the war I went back to Benson, this time on the Photographic Reconnaissance Development Unit, where I acquired a taste for research and development work which coloured my subsequent career.

A special interlude in his stay there was two Mark 34 Mosquitos, numbered RG300 and VL613.

In September, 1946 there was an Aeronautical Exhibition in Buenos Aires and the Foreign Secretary, Ernest Bevin, had arranged to send an aircraft from the RAF on a goodwill mission. There was the additional possibility of demonstrating our aircraft capabilities leading, perhaps, to sales of surplus production in the aftermath of the war.

The job came my way, to take a Mosquito PR 34 and, operating at maximum possible cruising speeds, to attempt the journey to Buenos Aires in 24 hours–including refuelling stops at Gibraltar, Dakar, Natal in Northern Brazil and Rio de Janeiro. So much for the intention.

South America was still in the 150 mph, not over 5,000 feet era, and we needed supplies of oxygen which was used from take-off to landing. Air Ministry arranged to position oxygen cylinders at our proposed refuelling stops and also at Buenos Aires.

My navigator for the trip was Flight Lieutenant Freddie Thayer, as good a crew and companion as one could ever wish to find. We talked to Rolls Royce about continuous high-power outputs from the Merlin engines and they recommended cruising at +7 lbs boost and 2,650 rpm, this being maximum weak mixture cruise, with normal climb power of +12 lbs boost and 2,850 rpm. The PR 34 had the normal inboard and outer wing tanks with 539 gallons, plus 328 gallons in the bomb-bay tank and two 100-gallon under-wing drop tanks–a total of 1,067 gallons, plenty for our longest leg across the South Atlantic. British South American Airways were operating the route with Yorks, and were very helpful with route information, particularly radio frequencies, also radio beacons.

It was already September when we first heard of the project, so time was pressing, and we finally took off from Benson on 22 September at about 4 a.m. We landed at Gibraltar after three hours 20 minutes, had a quick turn-round and off again into the blackest night I can remember. Even at 30,000 feet, no stars–and we had navigation trouble as we could not contact any of the French radio stations on the West African coast. We decided they had all gone to bed!

Coming up to ETA at Dakar, again we could make no radio contact with anybody and diverted to RAF Yundum at Bathurst, using their radio beacon for a homing. We landed and while waiting at the end of the runway for taxi instructions, the starboard wingtip was rammed by the Fire Tender, which then proceeded to spray the Mosquito with foam, under the impression that we were on fire. The PR Mosquitos had unshrouded exhausts, so there was a certain amount of flame visible, particularly on a very black night. I could sympathise with the Fire Tender crew, who were all local black men, because a York had crashed in flames off the end of the runway a week or so earlier.

Another aircraft, PR 34 VL613, was flown out for us to replace PR 34 RG300, and this we took on to Buenos Aires as planned, but some days later, arriving on 3 October.

The only oxygen cylinder we found in South America was at Natal in Brazil, so this curtailed our ideas of operating at high altitude, and speed was correspondingly lower. We gave a number of demonstrations around Buenos Aires, also at Cordoba and Mendoza. We created a stir when we returned from Mendoza to Buenos Aires in one hour 40 minutes, which was an unheard-of speed in those days for crossing the Argentine.

On 21 October we returned to Rio de Janeiro where we gave further demonstrations, until on 24 October the aircraft became unserviceable with a leaking radiator. This could not be repaired satisfactorily for a crossing of the South Atlantic, and so we had to await a replacement from Britain. We finally left for home on 15 November, arriving back at Benson by easy stages and some weather delay on 21 November. Our Atlantic crossing took five hours 45 minutes, which I understood to be the fastest crossing up to that time, but this was entirely unofficial and difficult to check.

There was no doubt that the Mosquito showed its sterling qualities both in performance and serviceability, and everybody we met was most impressed. I met the Argentine Air Minister before we left, and he expressed his thanks and admiration for the aircraft. He would have liked to obtain Mosquitos for the Argentine Air Force, but he pointed out that it was a big performance jump for the pilots and, furthermore, their airfields were not really suitable. I did slip in and out of some small grass airfields, so I could sympathise with his view.

In 1947 McCreith went as a student to the Empire Test Pilot's School, where there was a wide variety of Mosquitos; and then in 1948 to A. & A. E. E. at Boscombe Down, for a three-year tour of test flying, which also included various marks of Mosquito.

My final brief encounter with the Mosquito was

234

when I took over command of No. 81 PR Squadron at RAF Seletar, Singapore, in August, 1955. Shades of 680 Squadron in North Africa and Italy! The equipment was the Meteor PR 10 and the Mosquito 34–although the Mosquito was reaching the end of its days. The time in the tropics, plus sheer *anno domini*, took toll of the glued joints, so when I arrived aircraft were already being scrapped. I renewed acquaintance with V16 13 and was sorry to see it, too, go to the scrap heap.

The end of the war in the Pacific had seen the rise of successful resistance movements against the Dutch in their former possessions and also in Indo-China against the French (and subsequently, the Americans). Only in Malaya was the insurrection contained and the territory handed over in orderly fashion to the people who inhabited it.

With the Communist 'emergency' in Malaya the RAF squadrons of the Far East Air Force were all on an operational basis. Hence No. 81 was continuously flying operations in support of the Army in Malaya, which were code-named 'Firedog'. So there came the time when the Mosquito would make its last operational flight.

We made a little event of it out there, but I do not know if the press mentioned it at home. I thought, as a matter of Squadron morale, that it would be appropriate to give the task to the Mosquito crew who had been longest with the Squadron. So the job was given to Flying Officer 'Collie' Knox, pilot, and Flying Officer 'Tommy' Thompson, navigator, in Mosquito PR 34 RG3 14. I am afraid the one detail I cannot supply is the date! I have no record of when this happened and can only guess it was towards the end of 1955. I last flew a Mosquito on a 'Firedog' operation on 14 October, 1955, and of course I was busy with similar operations on the Meteor PR 10, so my Log Book gives no clues.

The date proved to be 15 December, 1955 (the campaign having begun in July 1949), but this was not in fact to be the final operational use of the Mosquito. Far from it.

CHAPTER SIXTEEN
Sinai War
(1948-1958)

In the War of Independence (1948–1949) the Israeli Air Force possessed a single Mosquito, a PR Mark XVI, which had been smuggled into Israel and was flown in action by a young French-Jewish pilot with Second World War experience.

Originally, two machines had been bought in England, NS 811 and NS 812, both of which had served with the American Air Force in the photo-recce role. They were given civil registration as G-AIRT and G-AIRU. On 5 July, 1948, the first of the pair was smuggled out of Britain, flown by John Harvey, an English pilot, non-Jewish, who was to be of great help to the tiny Israeli Air Force. After intermediate landings in Nice and Corsica, he arrived at Haifa airport, but the other Mosquito only got as far as Corsica.

As the Israeli acquisition of Mosquitos was often clandestine, absolute certainty as to their numbers is not possible, but it was not less than 80, five different versions being involved.

The inside story of the acquisitions has not been told, but that it was devious is obvious. For instance, in 1950 the Canadian government gave export licences for six Mosquitos and a contract had been signed with De Havilland Canada, when the American State Department said 'No!' (presumably because the engines were American-built). Nevertheless, one Mosquito got away, flown by Ray Kurtz and Seymour Lerner, but disappeared over the Atlantic in May 1951.

In France, the story was happier. After the Second World War the French had bought quantities of Marks III, VI, XVI and XXX; some of them went to war in Indo-China. In 1950, many were up for sale, mainly at the airfields of Chateaudun, Rennes and Tours, although some were in North Africa. David Orly, who flew some of these planes in the early to mid-1950s, commented:

> That was anything from five to ten years after they had been dumped in the far corners of out-of-use airfields in France and England. You can imagine the state they were in. It was a wonder that they held together as well as they did and that we had no more than two in-flight break-ups.
>
> I did spend a few years in the IAF flying the DH Mosquito, an aeroplane about which it is said the mechanics used a flute to perform their Daily Inspections. Of course, I never actually saw it, but at the dawn of every day, long before we pilots had crawled from between our rough army blankets, the mechanics were supposed to walk around the Mosquitos, playing their flutes to entice the worms to crawl out from the wood of which these aeroplanes were constructed . . .
>
> On 17 February, 1951 a contract was signed with the French to purchase 59 Mosquitos, of four different marks, paying $5,000 for a fighter-bomber stored in a hangar (and therefore in reasonable condition, considering), $13,000 for a serviceable training aircraft, and $200 for each aircraft considered completely unfit for use (but which might provide spares). Overhaul was carried out by workers hired from Nord and Hispano, with IAF personnel responsible for quality control. As pilots would be needed to crew them after they had been ferried to Israel (mostly by British pilots), half-a-dozen Israeli airmen were sent to England for a

conversion course, once the RAF had agreed to train one Israeli as an experiment. The need for diplomacy and discretion, in view of the Middle East situation, is obvious. This handful of trainees included David Orly.

I was among that group of six who, in November 1951, were sent to RAF Swinderby, in Yorkshire. I remember the impression on us green pilots as, on the day of our arrival at the RAF Station, we drove past one of the hangars and saw there a row of Mosquitos, all on trestles and without landing gear. Yes, they told us, once you get into a swing on landing you just can't keep the aircraft straight, and then the gear just folds sideways.

We returned to Israel early in 1952 as senior Mosquito Pilots (there simply weren't any more senior ones) and soon I found myself spending many hours in the right-hand seat of a Mark III–a dual-control Trainer. Like our English mentors, we did not shy from one-engine landings, with one prop feathered. It was on the downwind leg of one such circuit that I told my pupil to unfeather. Before I could count to two, he had feathered the good engine; and there we were at 1,500 feet, in a Mosquito with both props as still as telegraph poles.

The Mark VI was the main service aircraft. It was fitted with four Brownings and four Oerlikons, and had a rocket-launcher for four five-inch rockets under each wing. These could be replaced by racks for 250 kg bombs; and in a small bomb-bay behind the cannons two more 250 kg bombs could be carried. That was quite a weight for the two RR Merlins and left us with a one-engine-out climb performance of near zero.

The aircraft, of which there must have been about 60, were divided between two squadrons, one of which was given the additional task of training new Mosquito pilots both in flying these aircraft and in their operational use. I myself spent most of my time instructing.

Operationally, we placed emphasis on low-level surprise tactics. During such training flights we had some hair-raising squeezes, as a formation of four tried to manoeuvre in a canyon only comfortably wide enough for two. In the air one just cannot put one's foot on the brake pedal as one does in a motor car!

The CO of the Fighter-Bomber squadron was Yehezkiel Somekh, who summed up the period to June 1956 when the unit was closed down and the Mosquitos stored (only temporarily, as it happened):

We had been engaged in intensive training, taking into consideration the advantages of the Mosquito: two-man crew, long-range operational ability, and a heavy armament and bomb-load compared to other aircraft in the IAF. Our training consisted mainly of low-level long-distance night navigation and night attacks using live ammunition, with and without illuminating flares. As no war was foreseen at that time, the training was aimed to prepare the crews for the next generation of aircraft—the jets— and in fact they proved to be most valuable later in operating the French Vautour fighter-bomber.

The CO of the two squadron base, before it was temporarily de-activated, was Lieutenant Colonel L. D. Easterman, DFC, who had joined the RAF in September 1940 and, after a spell as a flying instructor, did an operational tour on Lancasters in 1944 and 1945. In 1946 he left the RAF; and in 1949 he went to Israel and became CFI and CO of the flying school.

240

In 1945 I became commander of the operational base which had two Mosquito squadrons, and learned to fly the Mosquito, which had been my ambition in the RAF. I consider it was an important aircraft, which had an effect on the war; more so than the Me 262.

In 1954 and 1955 I did a number of photo recces and armed recces over Sinai, the Canal Zone, and Southern Syria. During that period the Arab air forces were probably weaker even than they are today (1987). On photo-recce flights there was no AA whatsoever, and no interception.

However, on one armed night recce over Sinai in 1955 there was a certain amount of AA because we made it at low-level–around 300 feet. It was all light AA, but we were not hit. Back at briefing I astonished my navigator when I reported 'light to medium' intensity AA. He, not having been under fire before, was speechless at this; but for me there had been less tension than when flying a Lancaster, because the enemy defences were less formidable than I had been used to.

In the beginning, we had had just a few Piper Cubs, but soon achieved complete superiority, except for the Yom Kippur War when missiles were introduced. Apart from that, the ratio of losses between the Israeli and Arab Air Forces was incredible. In 1982, 60 Syrian machines were shot down, and not one Israeli aircraft. Yes, you could expect to get taken prisoner, but those of us who fell into Syrian hands had a bad time. At present, the Israeli Air Force is probably the most battle-experienced in the world.

I left the IAF for El-Al in 1956, and didn't fly Mosquitos during the Sinai campaign. Instead I was adviser to the Commander of the Northern Front during the tank battles. One didn't know what was going on and therefore it was more frightening than air war.

One flank of the Southern Front was the Sinai desert, but the word 'desert', conjuring up for many an image of rolling sand dunes and an oasis or two among clustered palm trees, has no reality in fact. David Orly's reference to flying down narrow 'canyons' is the truth. It is a mountainous desolation, the flanks of the hills scored by flash floods, with only a few tiny bushes dotted about in the valleys. This is the real Biblical 'wilderness', but in an unclouded, unpolluted atmosphere the stars are glitteringly clear and bright at night, and the deep water just off those barren shores–6,000 feet deep in some cases–is in contrast a rainbow world of fish and coral and sharks. This was to be the southern battlefield in 1956.

What is known in Israel as the Sinai War, in England is usually referred to as 'Suez' and associated with the downfall of Anthony Eden. By this time, the Mosquito was far from being the fastest aircraft in the world. Nevertheless, it was still useful. For Captain David Gatmon, who is still in aviation, with Tower Air Inc. at JFK International Airport, New York, mention of the Mosquito brings back many memories.

When the Sinai War broke out in October 1956, I was a Reserve Pilot in the IAF and had just started my career as a civilian pilot with El-Al. The Mosquitos were no longer in service with the Air Force and were stored in the Israel Aviation Industries.

As you may recall, the Sinai War was a joint venture of Israel, France and England, and was well planned in advance. I was called one day by my reserve unit and told that I should report to the Aviation Industries and ferry a Mosquito to Ramat-David, an Air Force base in the northern part of

Israel. Arriving there, I was called to the briefing room where I learned from General Dan Tolkovski, the Air Force Chief at that time, about the operational plans to attack the Egyptians in the Sinai. I also learned that the Mosquitos were reinstated as a ground support squadron for the sole purpose of the Sinai War. In comparison with the French fighter planes that Israel had at that time, the Mosquito had a good carrying capacity and, with its cannons and machine-guns, was suitably armed for this purpose.

For the first two days the Mosquito fighter-bomber squadron of 13 operational aircraft was kept on the ground in daylight because the air battles were being fought out over the Sinai. The distant Egyptian airfields, which would have been its targets had Israel been fighting alone, were being taken care of by the British and French. David Gatmon carried out an operation on the third day of the war.

On 31 October I was assigned the No. 3 position in a formation of four Mosquitos on a mission to attack Rafiach (RAFA) Airport in the Gaza Strip. RAFA was not an active airport, but the hangars were used for tank storage. My mission called for two consecutive low-level flights over RAFA, destroying hangars and all other storage buildings. On the first pass we would drop the one-ton bomb in the belly, followed by two more runs of rocketing and strafing. The first flight was uneventful. I had good results, and all cannons and machine-guns functioned well on my strafing runs. On my second flight, I released the bomb and shot my four rockets; but on the strafing runs which followed, my cannons and machine-guns did not respond.

I decided to wait for my No. 2 (we split to two

couples during the attack) to finish his strafing runs and then fly back together to base. As I was hanging around the airport, I was hit by an anti-aircraft shell which penetrated into the cockpit.

I was badly wounded in my right leg and hand, but felt I still had control of the aircraft. By this time my No. 2 had finished his strafing runs and joined me for the return flight to base. I told him what had happened to me and asked him to come close under me and assess the damage. The only thing he could see was a relatively large hole, nothing else. However, he suggested that I should land as soon as possible as I was badly wounded.

However, I felt uncomfortable about flying to another base. There was a lot of activity with French and British aircraft above me. I did not know the proper frequencies for the southern airports and I did not want to climb to a higher altitude without knowing what the traffic was. So we stayed at low-level over the Mediterranean, heading north to Ramat-David. I made it safely and was rushed to the hospital, where I stayed for one month.

I was told later by my No. 2, who came to visit me there, that the chain connecting the ailerons on my aircraft was torn on the bottom side, and I was lucky I did not lose control, as I would not have had a chance to evacuate the plane on a low-level flight. So the good old Mosquito did not betray me. Today, we have all the advanced jet fighters around, but the Mosquito was a super fighter for its time and I really feel proud to be part of this wonderful history.

Yehezkiel Somekh, the CO of the fighter-bomber squadron, pointed out that they had three roles. Firstly, long-distance day and night patrol and attack operations over the Suez Canal area and the Sharm El Sheikh Strait (alternatively known as the Straits of Tiran). Secondly, the task of escorting the two B-17 Flying Fortress bombers still operating in the IAF. Thirdly, and accidentally, a dramatic and successful rescue of a Mystere IV pilot who had been shot down in the area of Sharm El Sheikh, and was subsequently to become commander of the IAF. This was Squadron Leader Benny Peled, who had bailed out. The leader of a Mosquito formation was ordered to the rescue; and when he got there saw two Egyptian armoured vehicles approaching the crash site, which he discouraged with rockets. This prevented them taking Benny Peled prisoner and allowed time for him to be picked up by a Piper Cub.

Somekh confirmed the surprising survivability of the Mosquito, 16 years after it first flew.

> In all the squadron's operations, not a single aircraft was lost and only one crew member was injured. Although many aircraft were hit and damaged, few had to crash-land. Although built for a short lifespan in WW2, with experience the IAF obtained high serviceability; in the Sinai War it was 100 per cent–except for those badly damaged by enemy action. Apart from our Fighter-Bombers the IAF possessed the reconnaissance version which had a major role in obtaining the information needed for such a complex activity as the Sinai War. But I am not qualified to describe that aspect.

Although 31 October was the first day the whole squadron engaged in operations, the CO had gone out on a night operation before that, identifying Egyptian columns on the Gidi and northern axes, and attacking the longest column. A second Mosquito took off on a similar mission. For variety, the squadron was put on readiness to attack the Egyptian destroyer *Ibrahim Al Awal* next morning, but this was cancelled.

The usual targets were troop and vehicle columns. A

regular objective was Sharm El Sheikh, almost at the tip of the Sinai peninsula, which was a minor Egyptian naval base and the objective of a lightning strike from Eilat of the Israeli 9th Brigade. Later, it became a famous centre for underwater exploration of the Red Sea, with no sign apparent of its recently exciting past. David Orly recalled:

From Ramat-David we carried out our missions against the Egyptian Army in the Sinai. It was then that we began to appreciate that second engine of ours. The Egyptians did not have very sophisticated anti-aircraft defences, but their soldiers were told that during an attack from the air they were to shoot, each one, whatever arms might be in his possession. And so, when flying over an Egyptian position, the air would be full of rifle bullets. Our Mosquitos were the only aircraft which, though crippled, invariably made it back home.

Utilising the good high-altitude performance of the Mark XVI, with its two-stage, two-speed supercharged Merlins, we carried out extensive reconnaissance in our part of the world. Sitting by the window of a Boeing 747 the other day, and watching from 33,000 feet the Arabian deserts drift by below, it actually triggered some memories of those days, when at that altitude we used to sit in an unpressurised aircraft, trying to keep the wings level as the big cameras clicked away in the belly. Talking under those conditions was really weird, as the quantity of air passing by the vocal cords was quite insufficient to create any sound.

During those photo-recce sorties we stayed airborne for anything up to five and a half hours. It was a tedious job: flying to the target area, then flying up and down for one or two hours, and then back home again. Most of the time we had good radio contact with our own controllers, who were keeping their radar eyes open for us–with what primitive equipment there was in those days. When out of their range there wasn't anything else to do but look around.

After the Sinai campaign we continued with our photo-recces in the area, but the MIG 15s and MIG 17s in the Egyptian and Syrian air forces robbed us of our performance superiority, and soon the Mossie was replaced in this role as well as the fighter-bomber one. Nevertheless, during these operations, the last of which I did in the Mossie in August, 1958, I never saw one belligerent aircraft in my vicinity.

Even after being grounded our Mossies continued to serve. They found their way, though stripped of all their fighting gear, to the children's playgrounds in the Kibbutzim all over Israel.

During its service in Israel there were many landing accidents, but the most famous had nothing to do with the aircraft itself. During an approach to land during a rainy winter night in 1954–55, the machine was struck by lightning. It came down in flames in a ploughed field beside the runway and the ammunition began to explode, the crew being still inside. In spite of the flames and the exploding cartridges a young nurse, Esther Arditi, rescued both the injured men. The pilot, Ya'acov Solomon, was to recover, but the navigator died.

The most difficult machines to fly were the 'Black Mosquitos', the Mark XXX night-fighters. These were heavier and more complicated and the larger nose to house the radar impaired manoeuvrability. This version would not maintain height on one engine. There were also maintenance problems with the airframe. The black paint caused the aircraft to get very hot in the Middle Eastern sun and its ribs swelled; the tail surfaces and controls were particularly affected.

But nevertheless the Mosquito was a milestone in Israeli war aviation. It questioned the simple division into large lumbering bombers with great offensive power and small, nippy, short-ranged and lightly-armed fighters.

Hugo Marom was one of the pioneers of the IAF and is still in the business as Hugo Marom Aviation Consultants Ltd of Tel-Aviv. When John Harvey was killed flight-testing one of the Mosquitos bought from the French, Marom was sent out to take his place–which meant checking the work done in France to make the aircraft serviceable again after long disuse. He also led the squadron of Mosquitos in which David Gatmon served during the Sinai campaign.

I flew Mosquito Mark IIIs, VIs, XVIs and XXXIIIs in the Israeli Air Force, commanded a night-fighter squadron and ferried many of them from France and the UK.

In spite of having flown more than 150 types of aircraft, many as a test pilot, the Mosquito was undoubtedly one of the finest aircraft I have ever flown.

The Israeli Air Force has a museum of aircraft it used over the 39 years since independence, but it is still looking for a Mosquito. Should you know of a flying one that would be available, I would very much appreciate your letting me know.

In fact, there are a few highly-prized Mosquitos which are flyable, and the very first Mosquito of all is still preserved at Salisbury Hall, near Hatfield, where the design began to take shape. And that is another story in itself.

CHAPTER SEVENTEEN
Mosquito Museum (1958-1988)

A number of people helped to save the first Mosquito (or most of it). Two of them were W. J. Goldsmith, a former captain in the Royal Marines, and his wife Audrey. Mrs Audrey Goldsmith explained that her late husband's first love had been the RAF. But in 1939 the RAF had been difficult to get into, and the phoney War seemed just to go on and on, the waiting quite endless. One day Walter Goldsmith was passing a Royal Marine recruiting office in Edgware, London, and was tempted. He went inside and was told that yes, indeed, they did have a vacancy– for a cook at Eastney Barracks, Portsmouth. The Marines were (and are) a crack fighting unit, so he joined.

According to Walter, he got his commission by playing cricket. His batting brought him to the attention of the Brigadier, who felt that a good cricketer was wasted as a cook; and so he wound up as an officer in Landing Craft. In this way he met Audrey, who at the time was a Torpedo Wren at Dartmouth.

The involvement with aviation came much later, and that, too, can be put down to cricket. The pair had decided that they wanted to live in the country and, while Walter was playing cricket in the Hatfield area, he packed Audrey off with a map to see if there were any suitable tumbledown old houses which they might have fun renovating. This was the sort of creative home-making which appealed to them. At the end of a very hot day Audrey found Salisbury Hall–a derelict property set in a jungle of high grasses and weeds, ringed by a half-choked moat. But they discovered that there would be a bonus in renovating, for the Hall was a scheduled ancient monument under the care of the Ministry of Works, and they could live there free while putting the place in order, provided that they would open the building to the public for a specified number of days a year.

So they moved into two rooms initially, camping like gipsies in what they were given to understand was an old haunting place for Nell Gwynne; they did not suspect that the Hall had a much more modern history. In due time they discovered that, as Walter told Edward Bishop, the author of *Wooden Wonder*, 'the Mosquito aircraft had been designed in the ballroom, and the prototype was built on the cabbage patch'.

Mosquito W4050 was saved initially by F.E.N.St Barbe, then Business Director of De Havilland's. Towards the end of the Second World War he had the idea of turning a small hangar on the perimeter of the aerodrome, conveniently near the Hatfield by-pass, into a reception area which would impress visitors by displaying some historic Hatfield products–starting with a Cirrus Moth of about 1925 and a Dragon Rapide, then prototypes of the Hornet (the ultimate derivative of the Mosquito), the Sea Vampire, and finally W4050, the prototype Mosquito. This latter De Havilland's bought from MAP for £5 (including spare engines and propellors).

This splendid scheme struck the first snag when the hangar was wanted for building the Blue Streak rocket (subsequently cancelled, of course). The first casualty was the DH Hornet prototype, which was ordered to be burned; and *was* burned. However, the Sea Vampire was saved by W. J. S. 'Bill' Baird, an assistant to the PR Manager; he persuaded the Science Museum in London to take it initially and it eventually turned up on display at the Fleet Air Arm Museum at Yeovilton in the West

Country. W4050 was still not threatened, being used for display purposes at air shows, along with all the equipment which the Air Staff might require a Mosquito to carry. At the suggestion of C. Martin Sharp, the PR Manager, to the litter of drop tanks, bombs, rockets and rocket rails, cameras, etc., etc., was added–one kitchen sink!

Years passed and W4050 was in retirement at Salisbury Hall, when De Havilland's decided to give up that stately home. Bill Baird was asked please to remove that Mosquito. He found a temporary soft standing for it on the perimeter at Hatfield–where some of the instruments 'walked'. The prototype made a series of temporary moves after that, cluttering up various sites, until eventually Bill Baird was told to 'burn it!'

At this time a colleague of Baird's, Mervyn Nixon, lived next door to Walter Goldsmith and his wife and learned that they contemplated moving into Salisbury Hall, adding that there were odd features about the property which they did not understand–for instance, an unusual form of aircraft wing drawn on the wall of the lavatory! When they learned that the Hall they were going to move into was the birthplace of the Mosquito and that the prototype still existed but was under sentence of destruction, everything suddenly dropped into place. Their 'ancient monument' would gain a dimension if W4050 could be put on display there.

To house it, a hangar was available for £800 and an appeal to all De Havilland's subcontractors raised £1,800, enough to buy the hangar and build a concrete floor to it. In September 1958 the prototype was returned to Salisbury Hall and went on public display on 15 May, 1959. Since then, it has been joined by 16 other examples of De Havilland's contribution to aviation.

Appendix

Summary of Mosquito Variants

The first Mosquito, W4050, had a great many alterations made, including re-engining, while the type was being evaluated. The generally accepted designations of the variants are as follows:

PR Mark I (Merlin 21 or 23). Unarmed photo-recce version based on W4050.
PR/Bomber (Merlin 21). Conversion to bomber of PR I, later re-designated B IV series i.
F Mark II (Merlin 21, 22, 23). Day and Night Fighter and Intruder, with 4 cannon and 4 m.gs.
T. Mark III (Merlin 21, 23, 25). Dual-control Trainer. Unarmed.
B Mark IV (Series ii) (Merlin 21 and 23). Day and Night Bomber. Conversions included Highball, Highball trials and 4,000-lb bomb carrier.
PR Mark IV (Merlin 21, 23). Day and Night photo-recce conversion from B IV Series ii.
B V (Merlin 21). Projected Bomber with 2 drop tanks or 2 wing-mounted bombs.
FB VI (Merlin 21, 22, 23, 25). Day and Night Fighter-Bomber, Intruder, Long-range Fighter. Four 20 mm cannon, 4 x .303 Brownings in nose; 2 x 250lb bombs in belly bay, 2 x 250 lbs bombs on wing-racks (later 2 x 500 lb on series ii aircraft; or 4 x 60 lb rockets under each wing; or 1 mine or depth-charge; or combination of drop tanks and weapons.
B Mark VII (Packard Merlin 31). Canadian Bomber based on B Mark IV. Used in North America only.
PR Mark VIII (Merlin 72/73, 76/77). Photo-recce version with two-stage Merlins. Conversions from Mk IV.
PR Mark IX (Merlin 72/73, 76/77). Photo-recce.

B Mark IX (Merlin 72/73, 76/77). Bomber with two-stage Merlins based on PR Mk IX.
NF Mark X (Merlin 61). Night Fighter with two-stage Merlins. Not produced.
FB XI (Merlin 61). Fighter-Bomber version of Mk X. Not built.
NF Mark XII (Merlin 21, 23). Night Fighter conversion of Mark II fitted with AI Mk VIII in 'thimble nose'.
NF Mark XIII (Merlin 21, 23, 25). Night Fighter with wing similar to Mk VI and AI Mk VIII in 'thimble' or 'bull' nose.
NF Mark XIV (Merlin 67, 72). High-altitude fighter based on Mk XIII. Not produced. Superseded by NF XIX and NF 30.
NF Mark XV (Merlin 61, 73, 77). High-altitude fighter with two-stage Merlins and AI Mk VIII.
PR Mark XVI (Merlin 72/73, 76/77). Photo-recce with two-stage Merlins and pressure cabin.
B Mark XVI (Merlin 72/73, 76/77.) Bomber with two-stage Merlins and pressure cabin.
NF Mark XVII (Merlin 21, 23). Night-Fighter with SCR720/729 or AI Mk X.
FB Mark XVIII (Merlin 25). Ground attack and anti-shipping Fighter-Bomber. Four x .303 m.gs. plus 1, Molins 6-pounder 57 mm gun or 8 60-lb rockets.
NF Mark XIX (Merlin 25). Night Fighter with AI VIII or X/SCR720 and 729 in 'thimble' nose, based on NF XIII.
B Mark XX (Packard Merlin 31, 33). Canadian version of B IVii.
FB Mark 21 (Packard Merlin 31). Canadian version of FB VI superseded by FB 26.
T Mark 22 (Packard Merlin 33). Canadian version of T Mk III, developed FB 21.
B Mark 23 (Packard Merlin 33). Projected Canadian bomber comparable to

B Mk IX.

FB Mark 24 (Packard Merlin 301). High-altitude Fighter-Bomber based on FB 21. Not produced.

B Mark 25 (Packard Merlin 225). Revised B XX with improved single-stage Merlins.

FB Mark 26 (Packard Merlin 225). Canadian version of FB VI and revision of FB 21.

T Mark 27 (Packard Merlin 225). Dual-control Trainer based on T 22.

Mark 28 Mark number allocated to Canada but not taken up.

T Mark 29 (Packard Merlin 225). Dual-control Trainer based on FB 26.

NF Mark 30 (Merlin 72 or 76). Development of NF XIX with two-stage Merlins. AI Mk X.

NF Mark 31 (Packard Merlin 69). The NF 30 with American Merlins. Project only.

PR Mark 32 (Merlin 113/114). High-altitude photo-recce with two-stage Merlins, pressure cabin and lightened and lengthened wingtips (Span 59 ft 2 ins). Based on PR XVI.

TF/TR Mark 33 (Merlin 25). For carrier operations, a torpedo-recce fighter or fighter-bomber.

PR Mark 34 (Merlin 114) and PR34A (Merlin 114A). Very long-range recce with two-stage Merlins. No armour or tank bullet-proofing.

B Mark 35 (Merlin 113A/114A). Ultimate day and night bomber. Conversions to target tug (TT 35) and recce (PR 35).

NF Mark 36 (Merlin 113/114, 113A/114A). Night Fighter with improved radar.

TF Mark 37 (Merlin 25). Torpedo-Fighter or Bomber. Post War.

NF Mark 38 (Merlin 114A). The Mk 36 with later engines and AI Mk IX.

TT Mark 39 (Merlin 72/73). Target tug conversion of Mk XVI for Naval use.

FB Mark 40 (Packard Merlin 31, 33).

Fighter-Bomber built in Australia based on FB VI. Conversions to PR 40.

PR Mark 41 (Packard Merlin 69). Two-stage Merlin recce built in Australia and related to Mk IX and 40.

FB Mark 42 (Packard Merlin 69). Prototype fighter-bomber.

T Mark 43 (Packard Merlin 33). Trainer similar to T III.

Production

Hatfield: 3,326
Leavesden: 1,476
Standard: 1,066
Percival: 245
Airspeed: 122
Chester: 96
Canada: 1,076 (Canadian sources say 1,133)
Australia: 212
Total: 7,619 (if accepted figures are accurate)

Overseas Sales

Australia: 46 FB VI and 29 PR XVI
Belgium: 2 FB VI and 18 NF 30
China: 205 Mk 26
Czechoslovakia: 19 FB VI
Dominica: 6 FB VI
France: 57 FB VI, 29 PR XVI, 23 NF 30
Israel: 80+
Norway: 24 Mk VI
RNZAF: 74 FB VI
SAAF: 2 F II and 14 PR XVI
Sweden: 46 NF XIX
Turkey: Mk VI and T III
Yugoslavia: 106 of various marks, incl 60 NF 38

NB *The figures for Israel have been given as 250 and 300; but as text establishes the number was at least 80, with a few more untraceable because smuggled, etc. It was not possible to check the other figures and these also may be in error.*

Acknowledgements

More than one hundred people helped me with this book, most of them witnesses to the events described. I must express my gratitude to them all.

For the History of the Mosquito

Earl Bathurst (Bathurst Estate Timber Mills); John Connolly (Ministry of Aircraft production); G. A. Coster (Historian, Aerial Photography); Angela Crampton (Relative of G. Holt Thomas); Ted Field (Molins Machine Co. Ltd); Stephen Flower (Historian, Brooklands Museum); Lt.-Col. G. A. Gamman (New Zealand Forestry Company); Michael S. Gampell (Son of contractor to D. H., Hatfield); Audrey Goldsmith (Salisbury Hall & Museum); Peter Haining (Aviation Historian); Stuart Howe (D. H. Aircraft Museum Trust Ltd); A. E. Hurren (D. H., Hatfield); W. J. Ince (D. H., Salisbury Hall); David King, MBE (D. H., Hatfield); Alex Vanags-Baginskis (Aviation Historian).

For the Bombing of the D. H. Factory, Hatfield (employees of D. H., Hatfield, unless otherwise stated)

Denis Austen (student pilot); Mrs Violet Collom (widow of Richard); Ernest Clark; J. Ebenhart; Leslie Frost; Don Harrison; Denis MacManus; L. F. Waller; Ronald and Ruby Wiseman; A. J. Young; W. J. Ince (D. H., Salisbury Hall); Jack Arliss (Policeman, Hatfield); P. S. Thompson (Policeman, Hatfield); Mary Anderson (Agricultural student); Harold Altman (145 Bty, 42 LAA Regt., RA); Kennet Jarvis (Finchley); G. R. Jones (12 years old); Jim O'Sullivan (12 years old); Patricia Quinn (9 years old, now Mrs Cantien); J. Evan-Hart (Local aviation historian); W/Cdr Ira Jones (*Tiger Squadron*, Panther, 1959).

Royal Air Forces*

S/Ldr 'Bill' Aston (544 PR Squadron); F/Lt Derek Bovet-White, DFC (487 Squadron); W/O Ron Browne (Instructor); WRAF Sylvia Cane (Balloon Barrage, Plumstead); John Clarke (264 Squadron); S/Ldr W. F. Clayton-Graham, DFC (235 Squadron); F/Lt Fred W. Crawley, DFC (139 Squadron); G/Capt John Cunningham DSO, OBE, DFC (85 Squadron); LAC F. Dyer (82 Squadron); F/Lt C. H. L. Foster (464 Squadron RAAF); F/Lt J. E. L. Gover, DFC and Bar (692 Squadron); S/Ldr Kenneth J. Gray, DFC (87 PR Squadron RAAF); W/Cdr 'Bud' Green (410 Squadron RCAF); John P. Hamilton (333 & 627 Squadrons); F/Lt Harry S. T. Harris, DFC (608 Squadron); AC1 Den Hodder (85 Squadron); S/Ldr Jeremy Howard-Williams, DFC (Fighter Interception Unit); F/O Jim Inskeep (618 Squadron); W/O John Jacobs (25 Squadron); F/Lt John Keeling, DFC (605 & 23 Squadrons); Mrs Kay King (Widow of F/Lt L. F. King, 105 Squadron);

*Ranks and decorations not always known

254

Captain Reginald Levy (105 Squadron); S/Ldr George Lord, FRAeS (235 Squadron); W/Cdr S. McCreith (680 & 81 PR Squadrons); Mike Morgan (Photo Officer, 681 & 684 Squadrons); F/Lt George A. Nunn, DFC (608 Squadron); W/O H. S. Painter (684 Squadron); F/O R. G. Pickles (25 Squadron); W/O Raymond H. Smith (605 Squadron & 151 Repair unit); W/O Robert Smith (89 Squadron); F/O T. L. Taylor (248 Squadron); F/Lt Mark Wallis (139 Squadron); F/Lt W. G. Woodcock (248 Squadron); Hugh Wooldrige (Son of W/Cdr J. de Lacey Wooldrige, 105 Squadron); F/O Alan Woollard, DFM (139 Squadron).

Polish Air Force

Capt. Wactaw Milewski (Keeper of Archives, Polish Institute and Sikorski Museum).

Miscellaneous

W. E. Cawthorne (R. Sigs, Nuremberg); A. Courtney (393 Searchlight Regt, RE); Advice re contacts: S. M. Coates, C. N. Henty-Dodd, Brian Lewis, John Lewis.

USAAF

Robert B. Helliger (360 Bomb Squadron); Robert R. Lopiano (Tail gunner, B-17); John O. Millham (457 Bomb Group, POW); Claude C. Moore (25 Bomb Squadron); Leslie E. Veit (86 Air Transport Squadron).

Luftwaffe

Bernd-Dieter Barbas (Historian); Horst Deiner (Nachtjagdzentrale); Hptmn M. A. Diefenbach (Militärgeschichtliches Forschungsamt, Freiburg); Oberst Karl Hoffmann (Kommandeur, Flakturmes Friedrichshain); J. Howrath (German Embassy, London); Oblt Fritz Krause (I/NJG 10); Klaus H. Krebs (JG in France); Hermann Kuhnert (Kamaradschaft des ehem. Flakregiments 12); Klemens Rausch (I/JG l); Hptmn Heinz Rökker (I/NJG 2); Major Paul Zorner (III/NJG 5).

Israeli Air Force

Lt.-Col. L. D. Easterman, DFC; Brig. Y. Even (Embassy of Israel, London); Capt. David Gatmon; Hugo Marom; David Orly; Yehezkiel Somekh.

I am also indebted to the editors of *The Evening Standard*, London, *The News*, Portsmouth, *Flypast*, *8th Air Force News*, *Jagerblatt*, and the *Jerusalem Post* for their kind co-operation in tracing witnesses; and, as ever, to the prompt and efficient staff of the Public Library, Hayling Island, in obtaining the loan of specialist books.

Translations and Foreign Correspondence

I am indebted, as usual, to Ilse McKee for correspondence abroad and for translations from German and French; and to Lt.-Col. L. D. Easterman for translations of Israeli documents.

All Futura Books are available at your bookshop or
newsagent, or can be ordered from the following address:
Futura Books, Cash Sales Department,
P.O. Box 11, Falmouth, Cornwall TR10 9EN.

Please send cheque or postal order (no currency), and
allow 60p for postage and packing for the first book
plus 25p for the second book and 15p for each additional
book ordered up to a maximum charge of £1.90 in U.K.

B.F.P.O. customers please allow 60p for
the first book, 25p for the second book plus 15p per
copy for the next 7 books, thereafter 9p per book

Overseas customers, including Eire, please allow £1.25
for postage and packing for the first book, 75p for the
second book and 28p for each subsequent title ordered.